Growth and Change in Plants

P9-CRQ-174

Grades 2-3

Written by Diane Schlichting
Illustrated by Pat van Asteren

ISBN 1-55035-672-0
Copyright 2000
Revised December 2005
All Rights Reserved * Printed in Canada

Published in the United States by:
On the Mark Press
3909 Witmer Road PMB 175
Niagara Falls, New York
14305
www.onthemarkpress.com

Published in Canada by:
S&S Learning Materials
15 Dairy Avenue
Napanee, Ontario
K7R 1M4
www.sslearning.com

Look For OTHER SCIENCE UNITS

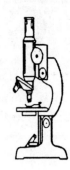

GROWTH and CHANGE in Plants

Table of Contents

GROWTH and CHANGE in Plants

Learning Expectations

Students will:
1. be able to identify the major parts of plants.
2. classify plants according to visible characteristics.
3. observe and describe the various lifecycles of various plants.
4. discover how plants adapt to their environment.
5. conduct experiments to demonstrate how changes in the environment (light, water, soil) affect growth.

Resources

Books:

- Burnie, David Eyewitness Books - <u>Tree</u>. Stoddart Publishing Company; © 1988
- Hickman, Pamela <u>The Kids Canadian Plant Book</u>. Kids Can Press; © 1996
- Hickman, Pamela <u>The Kids Canadian Tree Book</u>. Kids Can Press; © 1995
- Kalman, Bobbie <u>How a Plant Grows</u>. Crabtree Publishing Company; © 1997

Computer Software:

Encarta 1998 Encyclopedia, Microsoft Corporation; © 1998

The Internet:

The Internet is a valuable resource for both teachers and students. There are many good sites on the WWW about plants, some of which are student friendly. Most sites are for teachers and parents and would serve as a useful tool for research. Because of the changing nature of the Internet, specific sites are not listed here, but you can find them easily enough by going to "Yahoo!" or any other search engine and typing in key words.

GROWTH and CHANGE in Plants

Vocabulary

Parts of a Plant:
anther, bark, blossom, branch, bud, bulb, chlorophyll, embryo, fibrous root, flower, fruit, grain, leaf, leaves, nut, petal, pistil, pollen, roots, sap, seed, sepals, spore, sprout, stamen, starch, stem, tap root, thorn, trunk, tuber, twig, wood

Types of Plants:
bush, fern, flower, fruit, grass, lichen, moss, shrub, tree, vegetable, vine, weed

Plant Words:
annual, biennial, botanist, botany, carbon dioxide, carnivorous, color, coniferous, cultivate, deciduous, distribute, edible, erosion, fertilize, florist, fragrance, garden, gardener, germination, greenhouse, insectivorous, minerals, oxygen, perennial, photosynthesis, poisonous, pollinate, prune, reproduce, scent, soil, transpiration, water

Herbs:
balm, basil, bitters, boneset, caraway, catnip, fennel, geranium, horehound, horseradish, lavender, marjoram, mint, parsley, peppermint, rosemary, saffron, sage, spearmint, tansy, thyme, vanilla

Trees:
alder, ash, aspen, beech, birch, cedar, chestnut, coffee, elm, fir, hemlock, hickory, juniper, maple, oak, palm, pecan, pine, redwood, spruce, tulip, willow, yew

Shrubs:
azalea, bayberry, dogwood, forsythia, hydrangea, lilac, mock orange, pussy willow, snowball, spirea, sumac, yucca

Weeds:
bindweed, burdock, Canada thistle, dandelion, goldenrod, hemlock, horsetail, lamb's quarter, lupine, milkweed, nettle, plantain, poison ivy, poison oak, purslane, ragweed, St. John's wort, sorrel, stickseed, teasel, thistle, tumbleweed

Wild Flowers:
bellflower, black-eyed Susan, bloodroot, buttercup, cowslip, daisy, dandelion, fireweed, goldenrod, Jack-in-the-pulpit, lupine, spring beauty, toadflax, trillium, violet

Garden Flowers:
aster, babies'- breath, bleeding heart, chrysanthemum, crocus, daffodil, dahlia, geranium, gladiolus, hollyhock, iris, lily, marigold, morning glory, nasturtium, pansy, petunia, phlox, poppy, rose, snapdragon, sunflower, tulip

GROWTH and CHANGE in Plants

Teacher Information

Different Kinds of Plants:

There are many different kinds of plants, but they all fall into one of the following categories: trees, bushes and shrubs, weeds, mosses, and herbaceous plants (flowering plants.) Fungi and algae were once part of the plant kingdom, but are now their own kingdom as they differ in cellular structure, and because most algae and all fungi lack chlorophyll. Fungi also do not make their own food; rather they absorb it from dead or living matter.

Trees:

Trees are usually the tallest plants. They have fibrous roots and one long stem, called the trunk. They grow a new layer on the outside of the trunk every year. This outer layer is where the sap rises. The leaves make food for the tree by means of photosynthesis. Trees are either deciduous (lose their leaves in winter) or coniferous (evergreen.) They come in many different varieties, some of which are more accustomed to the tropics and most of which like the temperate regions of the world.

Bushes and Shrubs:

Bushes and shrubs are much smaller than trees and they grow from many stems, having a fibrous root system. They are often used as hedges and in yards for landscaping.

Mosses:

Mosses are small plants that grow on trees, rocks, deadfall, docks and anywhere else their spores land which is relatively damp. They do not have an extensive root system and can be either soft and feathery or dry and crumbly.

Weeds:

Weeds, the gardener's nightmare, are tough plants that grow wherever they can. They are often pretty with colorful blossoms, and can live in any soil or location. They have fibrous roots and leaves which contain chlorophyll. Although we often think of weeds as bad plants, they do have some benefits. Several species of weeds are harmless to animals and thus provide a safe food for grazers, whether wild or domesticated. Weeds also help prevent soil erosion with their wildly growing roots.

Herbaceous Plants:

These plants include wild flowers and garden flowers. They can be either annual, biennial or perennial. Many herbs belong to this group. These plants have stems, either tap roots or fibrous roots and leaves. Their flowers are colorful and attract insects and birds which help pollinate the plant. These plants often grow from seeds, but some may grow from bulbs.

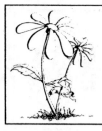

GROWTH and CHANGE in Plants

Leaves:

Leaves are the food-makers of plants. They contain chlorophyll, which is a green pigment. Although some leaves have other colors of pigment in them, these other colors only show up when the weather becomes cold and the chlorophyll begins to break down. Leaves contain many vein-like waterways that bring the water through the leaves and carry the new food to the plant. Leaves breathe in carbon dioxide and breathe out oxygen. They also expel water vapor. This is called transpiration. Leaves can grow singly on trees (simple) or in groups (compound.) They may grow opposite to each other or in an alternating fashion. Their veins can be either opposite or alternating as well.

Photosynthesis:

Photosynthesis is the process by which a leaf turns sunlight, air and water into a simple sugar that the plant uses as food. Chlorophyll cells help in this process by breaking down the components of air and water. The leaf uses heat energy from the sun to make chemical energy for the plant. This process takes place during two stages: a light dependent stage and a light independent stage.

Annual, Biennial and Perennial:

Plants that are annuals complete their life cycle in one year, from germination to flowers to fruit. Biennials take two years to complete their life cycles. They are usually just green in the first year and produce flowers and fruit in the second year. Biennials usually have strong root systems to keep them going to the second year. Perennials are plants that take three or more years to complete their life cycles. They have very strong root systems and produce a large amount of seeds. They flower and fruit every year after reaching maturity.

Plant Growth from Seeds:

Many plants grow from seeds. These seeds may lay in or on the ground for many years before germination takes place. Once germination has started, the seed sends its roots down into the soil to anchor the plant and to take in water and nutrients. The stem grows and leaves unfurl. The plant begins to make its own food. Once the plant reaches maturity, it will flower and, upon pollination, produce either fruit or seeds. Of course, the fruit of the plant contains seeds for propagation. Depending on the type of plant, at this stage the plant either dies, goes into its dormant stage or continues to thrive throughout the cold season until spring, when the cycle begins again.

Plant Growth from Bulbs:

Bulbs are different from seeds in that they have many layers of leaves covering the embryo plant. An onion is a bulb. Bulbs grow underground, shooting down roots, and the embryo within grows up out of the soil. The young plant sends a stalk of greenery up first, which will flower and produce the fruit or seeds.

GROWTH and CHANGE in Plants

Teacher Input Suggestions

Planning Ahead:

Before beginning the unit on "Growth and Change in Plants", try to collect as many of the following things as possible and make the necessary arrangements:

- various shapes and sizes of leaves (put them in a zip lock bag and store in the fridge to keep them fresh)

- samples of bark from different trees

- flower samples or photographs

- find books on plants in the school resource centre or public library for display and research

- cut out pictures of plants from magazines

- arrange for a trip to a conservation area or local forest for a nature walk

Bulletin Board Displays:

- Use your bulletin board for classification activities. You could post headings and word cards and have the students sort them into the proper categories.

- Make an attractive display of plant pictures, grouping by type or just creating a scene.

- Have your class paint or create a forest mural. Students can cut out plants they draw themselves or trace pictures and post them on the mural to create a forest scene.

- Use the bulletin board to create a Jeopardy-style trivia game. Categories could be posted with several questions below. Students could answer them individually or in teams throughout the unit for a grand winner at the end.

Introduction to the Unit:

- Show films to get the students' interest. Discuss with students the different types of plants. Brainstorm the five types and have lists of plants under each.

GROWTH and CHANGE in Plants

- Go on a field trip as mentioned previously. Even a walk around the schoolyard looking for plants is a good start.

- Read a story or poem about plants.

- Make charts with some of these suggested headings:
  - plants we eat
  - animals that use plants as homes
  - trees, bushes and shrubs, weeds, flowers, herbs
  - poisonous plants
  - deciduous and coniferous trees
  - trees in our neighborhood

- These headings can also be used for classification activities outside of the ones provided in the unit.

Graphing:

The classification charts can be used for graphing exercises in math. Organize the students into groups. Assign a classification chart to the students and have them devise questions about the chart that can be graphed. Or, students could graph plants seen in their neighborhoods at the local park, etc..

Science:

1. Aside from the many experiments in this unit, you can also build a terrarium in the classroom promoting local plant life. Gather plants, sticks, logs, moss, etc. from a forest and place them in a large fish tank or terrarium tank.

2. It is important to provide students with many hands-on activities with plants. They will learn the most from observing plant growth if they participate actively.

Discussion Topics:

You may wish to discuss any of the following topics with your students during large group sessions:

a) Any of the classification charts.

b) How plants are needed in our environment.

GROWTH and CHANGE in Plants

c) What we can do to preserve our forests and rainforests.

d) The food chain, of which plants are an important part.

Activity Center Ideas:

Independent activity centers should not be used until students have been well introduced to the information required to complete them. The Information Cards provided will give students a good base of information with which to complete the other activity cards. You may wish to use the Information Cards as your introduction to the unit instead of using them in a center.

Activity Preparation:

1. In the unit, activities for the following learning centers have been developed:

   Sounds   Word Study   Art
   Brainstorming   Research   Science
   Reading   Classification

2. Some of the activities are to be used as manipulatives. They should be cut out, colored, mounted on a sturdy backing and laminated. The pieces should be stored in an envelope with the activity card mounted on the front. Each manipulative activity has an accompanying instruction card.

3. Some of the activities are reproducible worksheets. These can be copied and put in a folder with the same worksheet attached to the outside for reference. The student will complete the assignment on the sheet.

4. Some of the activities are to be reproduced, colored, mounted on a sturdy backing and used as activity cards. The student will read the instructions and complete the activity on a separate sheet.

5. Most of the science cards require students to fill out a 'Science Journal' page. This page is the scientific method in language that young children understand. Students should complete the beginning of the page before they do the activity, the middle as they do it and the final section when the experiment is complete. They should not complete the entire sheet after the experiment is done. Teachers should model with the whole class how the sheet should be completed, using appropriate vocabulary and good sentences. This modeling may be done on a large chart, on a blackboard or on an overhead.

GROWTH and CHANGE in Plants

Activity Centre Preparation:

1. Prepare all activities to be used well in advance of the theme.

2. Make a sign for each center.

3. If space is a problem, activities can be stored in boxes or bins with a sign on the outside of each box. Otherwise, hang the sign above the table where the center is located.

Student Preparation:

1. Give students a book, duotang or folder in which to store their work. A file folder stapled along the short sides makes a nice holder.

2. Have students design a title page with the title of the unit, their name and date on the front. Decorate the page with plants of their choice.

3. Explain to students how the rotational process will work if you choose to use one. If you do not, explain how you want the activities done. Give precise timelines and follow each child's progress daily. Example: 3 activities, 2 days (depending on the amount of time spent on the unit.)

4. Teach your students how to organize their notebooks. Make sure that they use the title of each activity along with question numbers. Dates should be included, too. A date stamp may be provided if you find this more convenient.

5. Teach your students how to use the student tracking sheet. Make sure that they fill it out each time they complete an activity.

6. Each activity should be put into their books, duotangs or folders after it is marked and corrected.

7. At the end of the unit, the notebooks should be collected and the theme activities evaluated by the classroom teacher. Comments and observations should be noted on an evaluation sheet for each student.

GROWTH and CHANGE in Plants

List of Skills

Reading
1. Different Kinds of Plants
2. Parts of a Plant - Roots
3. Parts of a Plant - Stems
4. Parts of a Plant - Leaves
5. Parts of a Plant - Flowers
6. Parts of a Plant - Seeds
7. How Plants Grow
8. Plant Adaptations
9. Importance of Plants

Science
1. Diagram - Bean Plant
2. Diagram - Tree
3. Diagram - Flower
4. Growing A Bean Plant
5. Do Plants Need Light?
6. Do Plants Need Water?
7. Will Plants Grow in Anything?
8. How Do Leaves Change?
9. Inside a Bean Seed
10. Plant Waterways 1
11. Plant Waterways 2
12. Terrariums
13. Grow Your Own Vegetable Garden

Art
1. Bark Rubbing
2. Leaf Rubbing
3. Leaf Prints
4. Leaf Collage
5. Seed Picture

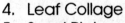
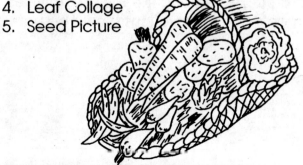

Word Study
1. Syllables
2. Alphabetical Order
3. Compound Words
4. Rhyming Words
5. Word Search - Vocabulary
6. Crossword - Word Meanings
7. Endings - s, ed, ing
8. Nouns/Verbs

Classification
1. Classifying Leaves Part 1 - Edges
2. Classifying Leaves Part 2 - Simple/Compound
3. Classifying Types of Plants
4. Classifying Edible and Non-Edible Plants

Sounds
1. Vowel Combinations
2. All Kinds of Blends
3. Double Consonants
4. Long "E"
5. Short/Long Vowels

Research
1. How Seeds Travel
2. Seeds or Bulbs
3. Terrific Trees
4. Fantastic Flowers
5. Water Plants

Brainstorming
1. Trees - Tropical/Temperate
2. Coniferous/Deciduous
3. Trees as Homes
4. Plants are Useful to Us
5. Colorful Trees

Teacher Tracking Sheet

Topic:

_____

Date:

_____

Evaluation Marks:
- S - Satisfactory
- I - Improving
- N - Needs Improvement
- U - Unsatisfactory

Students' Names:

GROWTH and CHANGE in Plants

Name:_____

Circle the number of each activity that you complete at each center.

Reading

1 2 3 4 5
6 7 8 9

Science

1 2 3 4 5
6 7 8 9 10
11 12 13

Art

1 2 3 4 5

Word Study

1 2 3 4 5
6 7 8

Classification

1 2 3 4

Sounds

1 2 3 4 5

Research

1 2 3 4 5

Brainstorming

1 2 3 4 5

Different Kinds of Plants

There are over 260 000 different kinds of plants in the world. Most plants fall into one of five groups: **trees**, **bushes** and **shrubs**, **mosses**, **vines** and **herbaceous plants**. Plants grow either on land or in the water.

Trees are usually the tallest of all plants, growing on one thick stem (trunk) with many leaves and branches. They grow in almost all kinds of soil and water conditions and grow in most areas of the world. Trees are **perennials**, which means that their life cycle is longer than three years. They come in many varieties and are either **deciduous** or **coniferous**. **Deciduous** trees lose their leaves as the cold season approaches and **coniferous** trees lose their leaves, or needles, throughout the year.

Bushes and **shrubs** are also **perennials**. They are usually much shorter than trees and have many woody stems. Bushes and shrubs grow all over the world and are either **deciduous** or **coniferous**. They are usually planted to help stop **soil erosion** and are very popular in gardens and parks.

Mosses are tiny plants that grow on rocks, soil, the bark of trees, in streams and in bogs. They have small, slender stalks and leaves. They do not have true roots and rely on ground water for survival. There are over 14 000 different kinds of mosses.

Vines are weak-stemmed, flexible plants that rely on other plants for support. They often wind themselves around branches and other objects to hold themselves up. Vines may be deciduous or coniferous and may flower or bear fruit. Lianas, vines found in the jungle, have very long woody stems that do not have leaves. They climb very high into the tree tops and grow their flowers and leaves up there.

Herbaceous plants are mainly flowers and flowering plants. This group also includes herbs and all the flowers that are commonly planted in gardens, grasses, and food plants such as radishes, lettuce, potatoes and gourds. Some of these plants are **annuals**, some are **biennials** and some are **perennials**.

Insectivorous plants are **carnivorous** plants. These plants gain some of their nutritional requirements from insects and other animals. Most of these plants grow in bogs or swamps. The trapping leaves on these plants are usually small, so generally small insects are the victims. When an insect lands on such a plant, it may touch small hairs that trigger the plant to close its trap where it will digest the insect. Others digest the insect with sticky liquids. Some insectivorous plants are the pitcher plant, Venus's flytrap, bladderworts and butterworts.

Different Kinds of Plants

Read **Information Card #1** called **"Different Kinds of Plants."**

Answer the following questions with a good sentence answer:

1. Name the five main groups of plants.

    _____

    _____

    _____

2. Describe the main characteristics of a tree.

    _____

    _____

    _____

3. How are trees different from bushes and shrubs?

    _____

    _____

    _____

4. What does perennial mean?

    _____

    _____

    _____

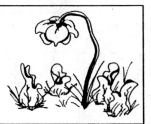
5. Where do mosses grow?

_____

_____

_____

6. Name six kinds of herbaceous plants.

_____

_____

_____

7. Describe an insectivorous plant.

_____

_____

_____

8. What does an insectivorous plant eat?

_____

_____

_____

9. Name three insectivorous plants.

_____

_____

_____

Parts of a Plant - Roots

Most plants have roots. The function of the roots is to **anchor** the plant to the ground and to absorb **water** and **minerals**. Roots are mostly underground and grow down into the soil. Roots do not have leaves, but they often have root hairs which grow out into the soil to help draw in water and nutrients.

Some roots are storage areas and food for the plant. Some examples are beets, radishes and carrots. The food stored for the plant is in the form of **starch**.

Some roots grow above the ground and help to support the tree. These are mostly tropical trees such as the "mangrove."

Roots are either **tap** or **fibrous**. **Tap roots** are roots that have one root that is larger than the rest. This larger root grows straight down. Beans, radishes and trees are examples of plants with tap roots. Plants that have **fibrous roots** have many slender strands of roots of similar size that spread out in all directions. Examples of plants with fibrous roots are corn and grass.

Parts of a Plant - Roots

Read **Information Card #2** called **"Parts of a Plant - Roots."**

Answer the following questions with a good sentence answer:

1. What is the main job of roots?

_____

_____

_____

2. What else do roots do?

_____

_____

_____

3. Name some roots that we eat.

_____

_____

_____

4. What type of food do the roots store for the plant?

_____

_____

_____

Reading Activity #2

Parts of a Plant - Roots

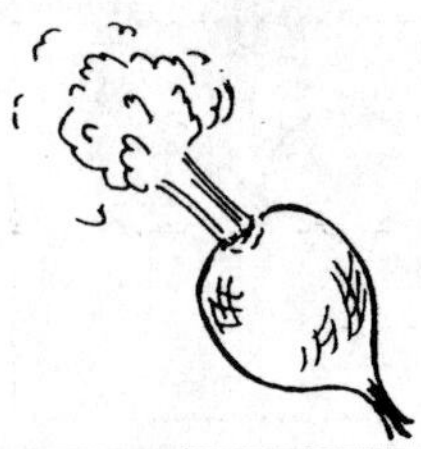

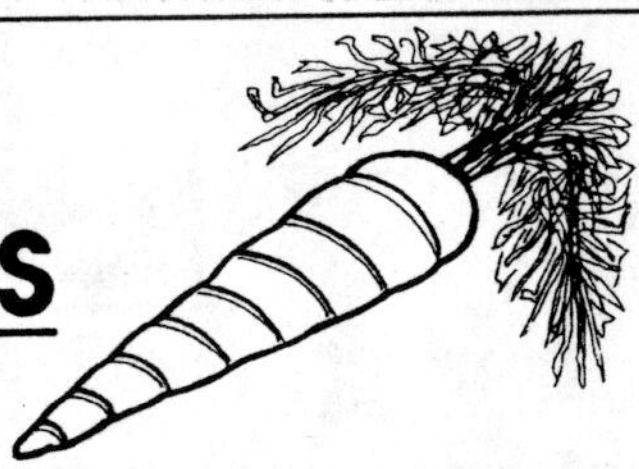

5. What is the name of a tree that has roots above ground?

6. What is the difference between tap roots and fibrous roots?

7. Name three plants that have tap roots.

8. Name two plants that have fibrous roots.

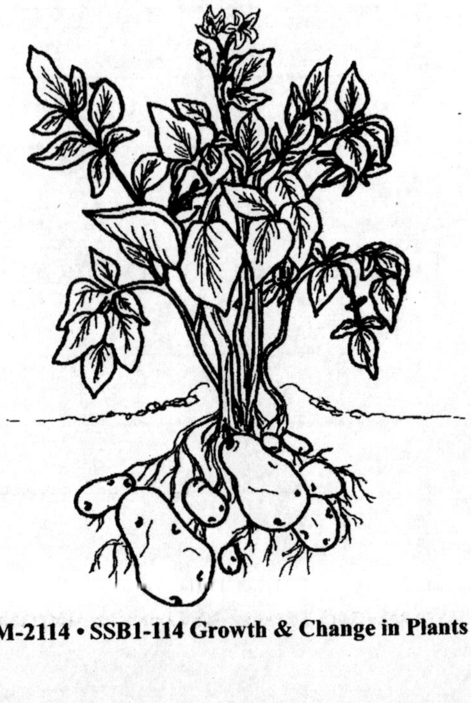

Parts of a Plant - Stems

Stems are the parts of the plant that usually have leaves and buds. They generally grow upwards and straight. Some, like the stem of the strawberry plant, grow along the ground. The potato is part of an underground stem.

Stems have **four** main **jobs**. They support the plant, they grow leaves, they provide food storage and they carry water and nutrients. In some plants, like the cactus, the stem makes food as well as storing it.

Some stems, like tree trunks, grow new layers every year, which is the outside layer of the stem. This is the layer that brings the food and water up to the leaves. The inner part of the stem is dead. As each year passes, the stem gets thicker and thicker as new layers are added.

Some stems, such as celery, rhubarb, broccoli, asparagus and sugarcane, are **edible**.

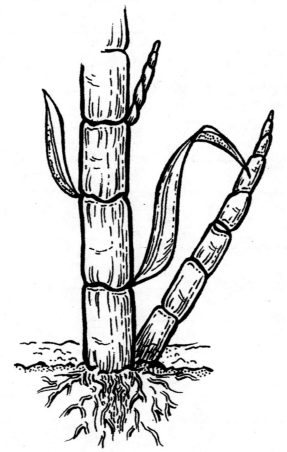

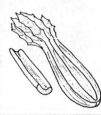

Parts of a Plant - Stems

Read **Information Card #3** called **"Parts of a Plant - Stems."**

Answer the following questions with a good sentence answer:

1. What do stems grow?

_____

_____

_____

2. What are the main jobs of stems?

_____

_____

_____

3. What do the stems of trees do?

_____

_____

_____

4. Name some stems that we eat.

_____

_____

_____

Parts of a Plant - Leaves

There are many different kinds of leaves with many different shapes. Each tree's leaves are unique in shape and size. Some leaves are long and thin, while others are broad and round, oval or heart-shaped. Some leaves have downy hairs on their underside and others are smooth. Some have jagged edges, some have particular smells and others are thin and feathery.

Leaves are often green in color because they contain **chlorophyll**, but they have hidden colors inside them. These leaves turn color in the autumn as the **chlorophyll** breaks down and exposes the other colors. The leaves then die and soon fall off. These leaves can be found on **deciduous** trees. **Coniferous** trees have needle-like leaves, whether in long, spiny needles or short clusters like the cedar. They remain green year round and are thus called **evergreens**.

Leaves have an important function: they produce food for the plant. This food-making process is called **photosynthesis**. During **photosynthesis** the leaf gets energy from the sun, and the **chlorophyll** helps to create a simple sugar from the air. The sugar and the water that the plant takes in make food for the plant.

Leaves breathe in **carbon dioxide** and breathe out **oxygen**. This is very important to humans as we need the oxygen that plants provide. Leaves also pass **water vapour** into the air. This is called **transpiration**.

Some leaves, such as lettuce, cabbage, brussel sprouts, mint, basil, dill and rosemary, are **edible**.

Parts of a Plant - Leaves

Read **Information Card #4** called **"Parts of a Plant - Leaves."**

Answer the following questions with a good sentence answer:

1. What are some of the shapes that leaves can have?

   _____

   _____

   _____

2. Why are leaves green?

   _____

   _____

   _____

3. Why do the leaves of deciduous trees change color?

   _____

   _____

   _____

4. What is photosynthesis?

   _____

   _____

   _____

5. Other than making food, what else do leaves do?

   _____

   _____

   _____

6. Name some leaves that we eat.

   _____

   _____

Parts of a Plant - Flowers

Flowers are the prettiest parts of plants. They come in all shades and colors and most of them smell very nice. Flowers are used to decorate rooms, whether in vases or in an artist's painting. Flowers, with their vibrant colors and wonderful smells, make the world beautiful.

Flowers don't just look pretty, they actually have a job to do. They are the **reproductive parts** of most plants. Flowers become **pollinated (fertilized)** and then produce fruit, which then creates the seeds required to start a new plant. Some flowers go straight to seed without producing fruit.

Flowers have many parts. The largest part is usually their **petals**. The petals are colorful and attract animals and insects that will help pollinate the flower. The scent of a flower also comes from the petals. This scent comes from an oil in the petals and may smell sweet or rotten, depending on the type of insect that it attracts.

Inside the petals are the **stamens**. The stamens are long, thin and stem-like. At the end of the stamen is the **anther** which produces the **pollen**. The long stem is called the **filament**. In the very center of the flower is the **pistil**. This bottle-shaped part of the flower contains **nectar** at the top and **eggs** at the bottom. The eggs will be fertilized by the pollen in order to produce **fruit** or **seeds**.

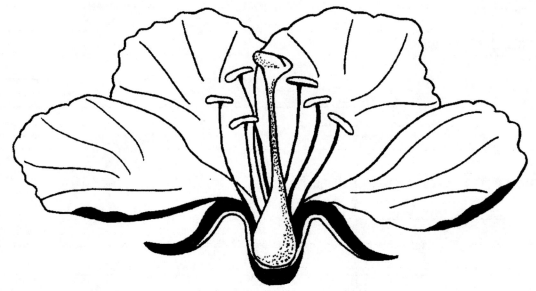

Parts of a Plant - Flowers

Read **Information Card #5** called **"Parts of a Plant - Flowers."**

Answer the following questions with a good sentence answer:

1. What is the job of a flower?

_____

_____

_____

2. What is the largest part of a flower? What does it do?

_____

_____

_____

3. What does the anther do?

_____

_____

_____

4. Describe the pistil.

_____

_____

_____

5. How do the eggs get pollinated?

_____

_____

_____

Parts of a Plant - Seeds

Plants **reproduce** themselves using seeds. Seeds come in all shapes and sizes, from the smallest, which are like the head of a pin, to the largest, which can be the size of your hand.

Seeds contain an **egg** that needs to be **fertilized** in order to create a new plant. Once the egg is fertilized, the plant then gets the seeds ready for travel. Plants **distribute** many seeds, sometimes several hundred. Yet most do not take root and grow a new plant. They may be broken, they may get waterlogged and they may rot. Other plants get eaten which destroys the seed.

Plants distribute their seeds in different ways. Some seeds fly with the wind, like maple keys and dandelion seeds. Some seeds have hooks and bristles that attach themselves to animals and people who walk past them. Burrs are an example of seeds that travel this way.

Other seeds travel by floating on lakes, streams or oceans. The coconut is a fruit that often falls into the ocean. It then travels to a new shore where it breaks open and the seed within takes root. Other seeds are distributed by animals that eat the fruit of certain plants. They pass the seeds as excrement. Plants, such as impatiens, have seed pods which explode, spraying their seeds in all directions.

Some edible seeds are sunflower, brazil nuts, coffee, corn, beans, peas and rice.

Parts of a Plant - Seeds

Read **Information Card #6** called **"Parts of a Plant - Seeds."**

Answer the following questions with a good sentence answer:

1. What is the purpose of seeds?

   _____

   _____

   _____

2. Why do some seeds fail to start a new plant?

   _____

   _____

   _____

3. List four ways that seeds travel.

   _____

   _____

   _____

4. Name five seeds that we eat.

   _____

   _____

   _____

How Plants Grow

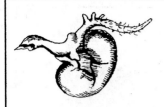
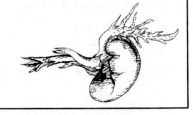

Nearly all plants grow from **seeds**. These plants are **pollinated** or **fertilized** either by another plant or by themselves. Some plants can **reproduce** without their seeds being fertilized, but these are not very common.

Seeds that are ripened fall to the ground where moisture loosens the seed cover. The seed then absorbs moisture and begins to swell. It is at this point that **germination** can take place. Germination occurs when a seed begins to grow or sprout.

Within each seed is an **embryo**. This embryo contains the tiny root, stalk, leaf and bud which will form the new plant when germination takes place. In some seeds, such as the orchid, the embryo does not form until after the seed has fallen from the plant. In most other seeds, the embryo has formed before it falls from the plant.

Once the seed has begun germination, it sends a tiny stalk up and sends a root or roots down into the soil. The roots draw water and minerals up into the seed to help it grow. As the stalk grows, tiny leaves open up and begin making food for the plant. The leaves spread wide to absorb the sunlight. The stalk grows taller, more leaves open and the roots continue to spread out, **anchoring** the young plant to the ground.

If the plant is a fruit-bearing plant, the young plant begins to grow buds in a couple of months. These buds open up and flowers appear. Insects and birds pollinate the flower and the fruit begins to grow shortly thereafter.

Some plants that grow in this manner are beans, peas, apples, and strawberries.

Most trees, vegetables, fruits and flowers are grown from seeds, but some plants grow from **bulbs**. These are made of a mass of leaves surrounding a short stem. Bulbs usually grow underground and produce a stem and leaves that grow above ground.

Common plants that are bulbs are onions, garlic, and several flowers such as crocuses, dahlias, tulips, hyacinths, daffodils and gladiolas.

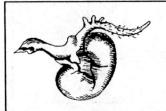

How Plants Grow

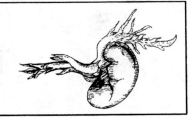

Read **Information Card #7** called **"How Plants Grow."**

Answer the following questions with a good sentence answer:

1. From what do most plants grow?

_____

_____

_____

2. What is germination?

_____

_____

_____

3. What happens to a seed when it falls on the ground?

_____

_____

_____

4. What is an embryo?

_____

_____

_____

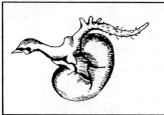
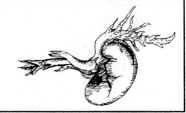
5. How does a little plant begin to grow?

_____

_____

_____

6. What grows from the flower of a plant?

_____

_____

_____

7. Describe a bulb.

_____

_____

_____

8. Name five plants that grow from bulbs.

_____

_____

_____

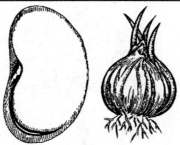

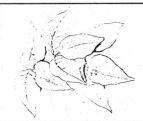

Plant Adaptations

Plants, like animals, need to adapt to their environments. They do this in many different ways, whether against the colder seasons or to defend against animals and people.

Most plants lose their leaves in the winter. Trees that do this are called **deciduous**. Many bushes and shrubs also lose their leaves when the frost comes. These plants go into a winter sleep, called **dormancy**. Although these types of plants look dead in the winter, they are not. Many of the plants that are dormant during winter need the coldness in order to grow again. These plants will not grow in milder **climates**.

Some plants are **poisonous,** which prevents them from being eaten by animals and insects. These plants have created a chemical inside their leaves or fruits that animals find distasteful or that will make the animal ill. Some of these plants are only poisonous at certain stages of their life cycles. "Sudan grass" is poisonous only when wilted or frozen.

Nearly every one out of a hundred species of plants are poisonous to humans. These plants will make people ill if they are eaten or even just touched. Some plants are poisonous throughout their life cycles and some are only poisonous at certain times. Various parts of the plant can contain the poison. Poison hemlock is poisonous throughout the plant, while the berries of the daphne and the foliage (leaves) of the wild cherry are the only poisonous parts of these plants. If a person eats a plant that is poisonous he/she can become very sick or even die.

Some plants have only to be touched to affect people. Nettle will cause a painful rash on the skin. Poison ivy and poison oak cause an allergic reaction that produces an itchy rash.

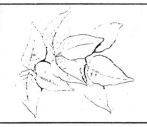

Plant Adaptations

Read **Information Card #8** called **"Plant Adaptations."**

Answer the following questions with a good sentence answer:

1. What are two things that plants do to survive?

   _____

   _____

   _____

2. What is dormancy?

   _____

   _____

   _____

3. Why have some plants become poisonous?

   _____

   _____

   _____

4. What parts of plants are poisonous?

   _____

   _____

   _____

5. What happens if you eat a poisonous plant?

   _____

   _____

   _____

6. Name two plants that will cause a rash if you touch them.

   _____

   _____

   _____

Importance of Plants

Plants have many uses which make them very important to humans. First and foremost, plants return oxygen to the air which we need to breathe. Without plants in the world, there would not be enough oxygen for us to survive.

Trees provide the raw material for paper and wood. Many different types of trees are used to make wooden products such as furniture. Some common trees are pine, cherry, walnut, oak, teak and mahogany. Trees are also used as raw lumber in building construction.

Plants provide us with food in the form of vegetables and fruits. Fruits grow on trees with the exception of tomatoes, cucumbers, pumpkins, and melons, and berries such as strawberries, blackberries, blueberries and raspberries. Fruit trees and plants flower before the fruit appears on the plant. Vegetables often grow low to the ground or even underneath it. Although squash is the fruit of the plant, it is considered a table vegetable.

Herbs are a special kind of plant that can be used for flavoring, to make teas or for medicines. Common herbs for food are thyme, sage, basil, rosemary and mint. Herbs used to make tea are camomile, hyssop, rose and goldenrod. Hundreds of years ago, herbs were one of the most common ways to treat illnesses. They are now becoming popular again. There are many herbs that are used for medicine, some of which are borage, digitalis, henbane, primrose, St. John's wort, garlic and camphor.

Plants are not only useful and helpful to people, but to animals as well. Plants are a main food source for many animals. Some animals eat grasses, some eat leaves and others eat the tender shoots from bushes and trees, while still others drink nectar from flowers.

Plants, such as trees and bushes, also provide homes for animals. Birds, raccoons, squirrels, chipmunks and other animals build their homes in them or use the dead, broken bits of plants, such as twigs, to make their homes. Some animals, like beavers, cut down trees to make their homes. Others, like woodpeckers, hollow out holes in the trees to build their nests.

Plants also protect the planet's surface. Roots hold the soil together and prevent **soil erosion**. Soil erosion happens when there are no plants to hold the soil. Water and wind wash or blow the soil away. This is a problem in the rainforests of the world today. Too many trees are being cut down and people are trying to farm the barren land. The rains in these regions are very hard and within a few years have washed away the good growing soil.

Importance of Plants

Read **Information Card #9** called **"Importance of Plants."**

Answer the following questions with a good sentence answer:

1. What is one of the most important uses of plants?

   _____

   _____

   _____

2. Name some of the most popular kinds of trees used to make furniture.

   _____

   _____

   _____

3. Which fruits do not grow on trees?

   _____

   _____

   _____

4. What are the three ways in which herbs can be used?

   _____

   _____

   _____

5. Name three herbs used to make tea.

   _____

   _____

   _____

Importance of Plants

6. Name four herbs used as medicine.

_____

_____

_____

7. How are plants important to animals?

_____

_____

_____

8. List three animals that make their homes in trees.

_____

_____

_____

9. What is **soil erosion**?

_____

_____

_____

10. How can we protect the land from soil erosion?

_____

_____

_____

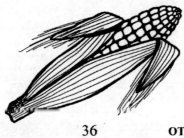

Science #1

Diagram of a Bean Plant

Cut along the dotted line that travels around the bean plant.

Paste the bean plant onto a large piece of paper.

Cut out the words and job descriptions below.

Paste them on the diagram to **label** the parts of the bean plant.

Color the diagram neatly.

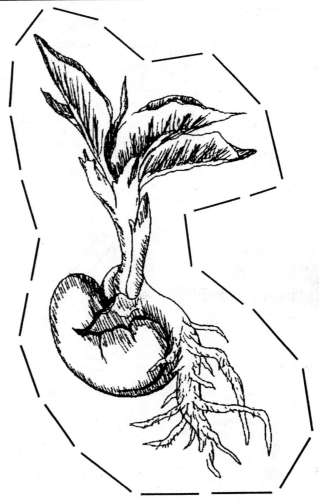

Stem	Roots	Leaf Bud	Leaf	Seed

• Makes food for the plant.
• Holds up the flowers and leaves.
• I started this plant growing.
• Bring water and nutrients from the ground.
• I will grow to be a new leaf.

Diagram of a Tree

Cut along the dotted line that travels around the tree.

Paste the tree onto a large sheet of paper.

Cut out the words and job descriptions below.

Paste them on the diagram to **label** the parts of the tree.

Color the diagram neatly.

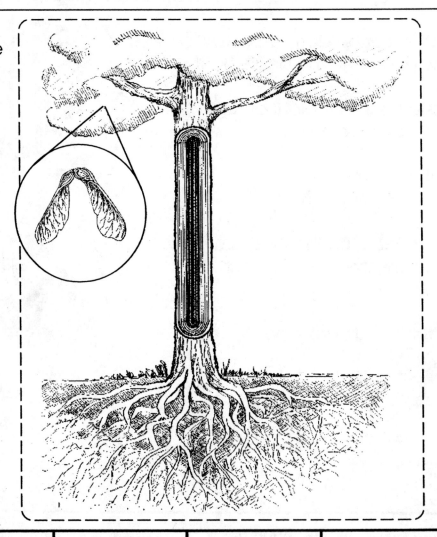

Leaves	Trunk	Roots	Bark	Seeds

• Make food for the tree.
• Holds up the leaves, fruit and seeds.
• Protects the tree from diseases and animals.
• Bring water and nutrients from the ground.
• Will grow to be new trees.

Diagram of a Flower

Cut along the dotted line that travels around the flower.

Paste the flower onto a large sheet of paper.

Cut out the words and job descriptions below.

Paste them onto the diagram to **label** the parts of a flower.

Color the diagram neatly.

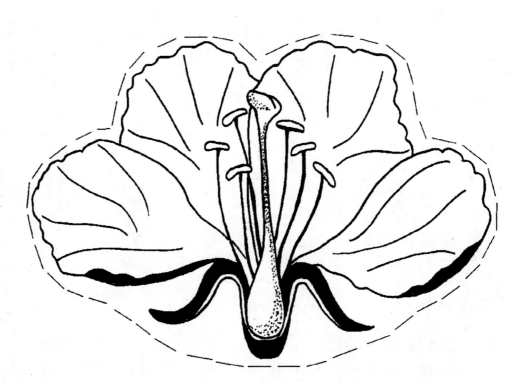

Petal	Stamen	Pistil	Pollen	Stem	Filament

- Seeds develop here.

- Color attracts birds and insects.

- Holds up the leaves and the flowers. Carries food and water.

- Supports the anther.

- Powdery substance used for pollination.

- This is found in the flower. It produces pollen.

Growing a Bean Plant

Experiment #1

Have you ever wondered how a seed grows into a plant? In this experiment you will watch a bean seed grow into a plant.

Materials:
- three bean seeds
- mason jar
- paper towels
- water
- soil
- small pots

Procedure:

1. If the bean seeds are dry, soak them in water over night. Crumple the paper towels and push them into the jar. Use enough towels to fill the jar.

2. Soak the paper towels, but make sure that there is no standing water.

3. Push the bean seeds down between the towels and the glass so that you can still see them. Space them out evenly.

4. Put the jar in a warm, dark place like a cupboard. Keep the paper towels damp.

5. When the beans have grown to about 5 cm tall (2 inches,) carefully remove them from the jar and plant them in soil in small pots.

Observations:

Answer the following questions on your recording sheet:

1. What happened to the bean seeds after a few days? After a week?

2. Make a graph to show the growth of your bean plant over three weeks.

3. Complete a **Science Journal Page** and put it in your notebook.

Experiment Journal

Experiment Title: _____

Date Started: _____ **Date Finished:** _____

Activity Answers

_____
_____
_____
_____
_____
_____
_____
_____
_____
_____
_____
_____

Diagrams of Experiment

Science Journal

I Wonder . . .

_____

_____

I Think . . .

_____

_____

I Will . . .

_____

_____

I Saw . . .

_____

_____

_____

I Learned . . .

_____

_____

Do Plants Need Light?

Experiment #2

Do plants really need sunlight in order to grow? In this experiment you will prevent a plant from getting sunlight and you will observe the changes that will happen.

Materials:
- two small plants
- tape
- marker

Procedure:

1. Label one of the plants "**LIGHT**" and the other plant "**NO LIGHT.**"

2. Put the plant labeled "**LIGHT**" on or near a window ledge where it will receive sunlight.

3. Put the plant labeled "**NO LIGHT**" in a dark cupboard or place a paper bag over the whole plant. Make sure that the plant doesn't get any light at all.

4. Observe your plants over the next two weeks, keeping the soil at the right dampness for the type of plant you have chosen.

Observations:

Answer the following questions on your recording sheet:

1. What happened to the plant in the cupboard after a few days? After a week? What happened to the plant in the light?

2. What differences do you see in the two plants after two weeks?

3. What have you learned about plants and light?

4. Complete a **Science Journal Page** and put it in your notebook.

Do Plants Need Water?

Experiment #3

Do plants really need water in order to grow? How much do they need? In this experiment you will learn about plants and how much water they need.

Materials:
- three small plants
- tape
- marker
- water

Procedure:

1. Label one of the plants "**NO WATER,**" the second plant "**SOME WATER**" and the other plant "**LOTS OF WATER.**"

2. Place the plants on or near a window ledge so that they get sunlight for two weeks.

3. Water the plant labeled "**SOME WATER**" whenever the soil seems to be getting dry.

4. Water the plant labeled "**LOTS OF WATER**" every day, keeping the soil wet.

5. Do not water the third plant at all.

Observations:

Answer the following questions on your recording sheet:

1. What happened to each plant after a week?

2. What differences do you see in the three plants after two weeks?

3. What have you learned about how much water plants need?

4. Complete a **Science Journal Page** and put it in your notebook.

Will Plants Grow in Anything?

Experiment #4

What kind of soil is best for plants? Will plants grow in anything? In this experiment you will plant seeds in several different types of soil and you will see which ones are best.

Materials:

- bean seeds
- marker
- pots with holes in the bottom
- tape
- sand
- potting soil
- clay

Procedure:

1. Put some sand in the pot.

2. Label the pot "**SAND.**"

3. Place three bean seeds on top of the sand. Spread them out.

4. Put a small layer, about (1 inch) 2 cm of sand on top of the beans.

5. Repeat the procedure with the "**CLAY**" and "**POTTING SOIL.**"

6. Place the pots near a window and water as necessary, keeping the soil slightly damp.

7. Observe the pots for the next two weeks.

Observations:

Answer the following questions on your recording sheet:

1. Which soil worked the best? How do you know?

2. Which soil didn't work? Why do you think that happened?

3. What did you learn about different types of soils?

4. Complete a **Science Journal Page** and put it in your notebook.

How Do Leaves Change?

Experiment #5

How do green leaves change to red or orange? Where does the color come from? In this experiment you will see that leaves contain colors other than just green.

Materials:
- green leaves
- baby food jar
- rubbing alcohol
- coffee filter

Caution: *Do not put the rubbing alcohol on or near your face.*
Do not drink it or put it in your mouth!

Procedure:

1. Tear up the green leaves and put them in the jar.

2. Pour some rubbing alcohol into the jar, just enough to cover the leaves. **BE CAREFUL!**

3. Cut a rectangular piece out of the coffee filter, about (1 by 4 inches) 3 cm by 9 cm.

4. Place the piece of filter paper with one end in the rubbing alcohol and the rest lying outside of the jar. Tape it if you need to.

5. Let this sit for about 10 minutes. Do not move it around.

Observations:

Answer the following questions on your recording sheet:

1. What happened to the green color in the rubbing alcohol?

2. What happened when you put the filter paper into the rubbing alcohol?

3. What have you learned about the colors in leaves?

4. Complete a **Science Journal Page** and put it in your notebook.

Inside a Bean Seed

Experiment #6

Have you ever wondered how a bean plant starts to grow? Inside every seed are all the things needed to start a new plant growing. In this experiment you will examine the inside of a bean seed to see how life begins.

Materials: • dried bean seeds
  • glass of water

Procedure:

1. Place several bean seeds in a glass of water.

2. Leave the glass to stand over night.

3. Carefully peel off the outer skin of the bean seeds. Lay it aside.

4. Very carefully split the bean seeds open along the crack. Use your fingernails to carefully pry them open.

5. Carefully examine the inside of the bean seeds.

Observations:

Answer the following questions on your recording sheet:

1. Draw a diagram of your bean seed. Label the following parts: **leaf, stem, casing, food storage, root, scar**.

2. Why is the food storage section of the bean seed so large?

3. Complete a **Science Journal Page** and put it in your notebook.

Plant Waterways 1

Experiment #7

Have you ever wondered how a plant brings the water up to its leaves? Plants have an internal waterway made of many tubes. These tubes bring water and nutrients to all parts of the plant. In this experiment you will see these waterways inside a stalk of celery.

Materials:
- celery stalk with leaves on top
- glass of water
- food coloring (red or blue)
- knife

Procedure:

1. Place some water in a glass.

2. Put several drops of food coloring in the water.

3. Put the celery stalk in the glass of water and leave it overnight.

4. Examine your celery stalk carefully the next day.

Observations:

Complete the following on your recording sheet:

1. Draw a **before** and **after** diagram of your celery stalk.

2. Using a knife, **carefully** cut the celery stalk in half crosswise.

3. Examine the inside of the stalk. What do you see?

4. Draw a diagram of the cross-section of the celery stalk.

5. How did the inside of the stalk get colored?

6. What does this tell you about how plants get water up to their leaves?

7. Complete a **Science Journal Page** and put it in your notebook.

Plant Waterways 2

Experiment #8

Flowers also have tubes that bring water and nutrients to their petals.   In this experiment you will see how these waterways extend right to the edge of a flower petal.

Materials:
- white carnations
- knife
- two glasses of water
- food coloring (red and blue)

Procedure:

1. Place some water in each of the glasses.

2. Put several drops of food coloring into the water: red in one, blue in the other.

3. Carefully slit the stem of the carnation up from the bottom so that the two pieces of stem will rest in the glasses, one in each color. Do not cut the stem completely apart.

4. Leave it overnight. Examine your carnation carefully the next day.

Observations:

Complete the following on your recording sheet:

1. Draw a **before** and **after** diagram of your carnation.

2. What happened to the carnation's petals?

3. Where is the red mostly visible? The blue? Are any other colors present? Why are the colors mostly visible where they are?

4. What does this tell you about how flowers use their waterways?

5. Complete a **Science Journal Page** and put it in your notebook.

Terrariums

Experiment #9

All plants need water to survive, but do you have to water a plant in order for it to grow? Find out in this experiment using terrariums.

Materials:
- bean seeds
- water
- tape
- soil
- two clear plastic cups

Procedure:

1. Place some soil in one of the plastic cups.

2. Put two or three seeds on top of the soil and add a little more soil to just cover the seeds.

3. Put a little water on the soil, just enough to make it damp.

4. Turn the other cup upside down and tape it to the one below. Make sure that the tape covers all the openings.

5. Leave the terrarium for several weeks, observing the seeds on a daily basis.

Observations:

Complete the following on your recording sheet:

1. Did your plant grow?

2. What did you notice about the inside of the top cup?

3. How did the plant grow if you didn't water it?

4. Where did the water come from?

5. How does your terrarium compare to a greenhouse?

6. Complete a **Science Journal Page** and put it in your notebook.

Grow Your Own Vegetable Garden

Experiment #10

Did you know that it is easy to grow your own vegetable garden right from the vegetables instead of from seeds? Try this in your classroom.

Materials:
- soil
- water
- tape
- marker
- potatoes with eyes
- pots with drain holes
- carrots with leaves on top

Procedure:

1. Place some soil in each of the pots.

2. Cut the carrots and potatoes so that each green leaf or eye has a piece of vegetable attached to it that is at least (1.5 in) 3 cm thick.

3. Plant the carrot in the soil so that the green leaf is above the soil.

4. Plant the potato so that the whole piece is below the soil.

5. Label the pots with the tape and marker.

6. Place the pots in a sunny windowsill. Water the plants as necessary.

7. After several weeks, carefully remove the plant from the pots. Examine the plants, then plant them in an outdoor garden or maintain them inside in a larger pot.

Observations:

Complete the following on your recording sheet:

1. Did your plants grow? What grew first? Last?

2. What happened to the piece of vegetable you had put in the soil?

Art #1
<u>Bark Rubbing</u>

<u>Materials</u>:
- white paper
- wax crayons
- a tree

<u>Method</u>:

- **Select** a tree with interesting bark.

- **Place** your paper against the bark of the tree.

- Using the side of the crayon, **lightly rub** the crayon over the paper so that you see the pattern of the bark.

- **Draw** a picture of your tree at the side.

- **Look up** your tree in a book and **write** its name underneath your rubbing.

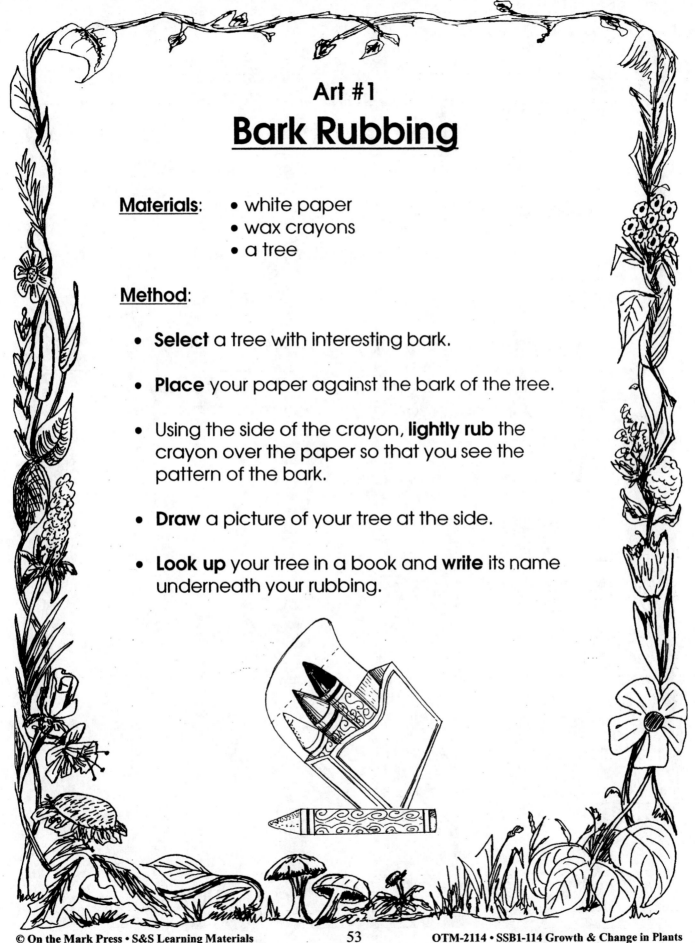

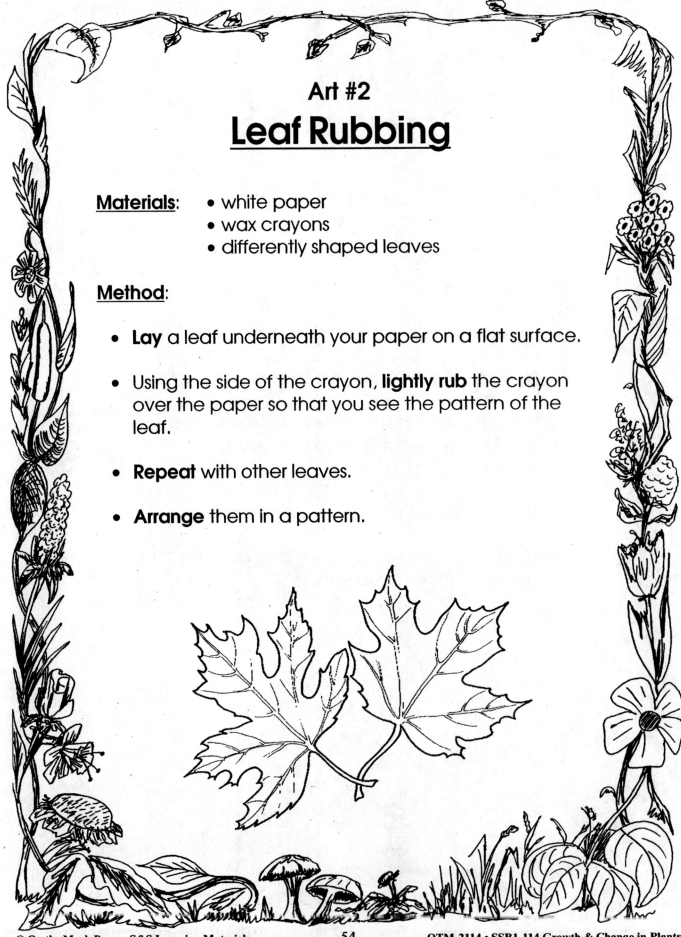

Art #2
<u>Leaf Rubbing</u>

<u>Materials</u>:
- white paper
- wax crayons
- differently shaped leaves

<u>Method</u>:

- **Lay** a leaf underneath your paper on a flat surface.

- Using the side of the crayon, **lightly rub** the crayon over the paper so that you see the pattern of the leaf.

- **Repeat** with other leaves.

- **Arrange** them in a pattern.

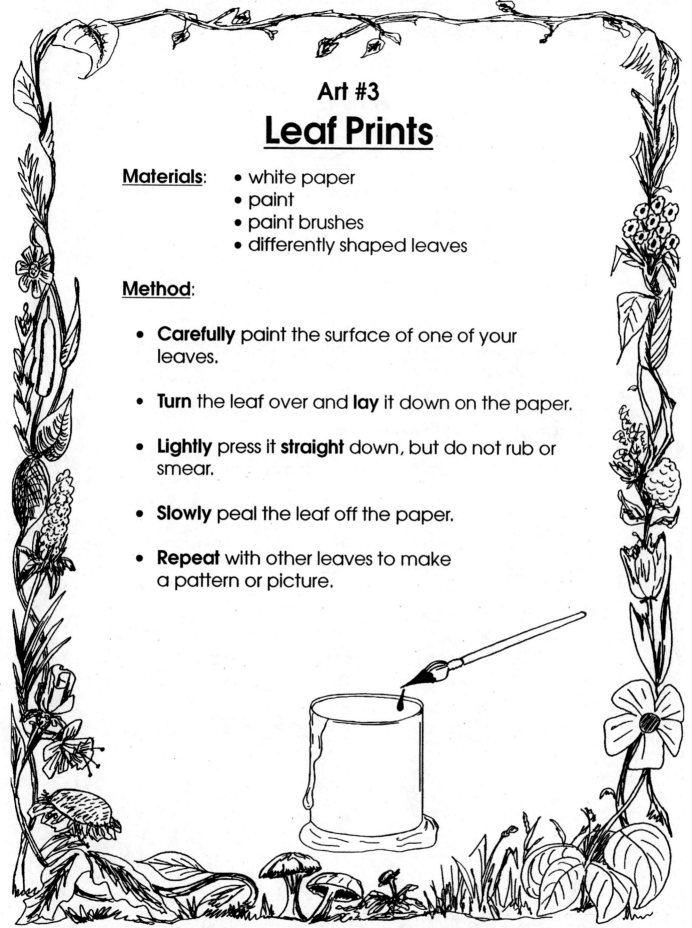

Art #3
<u>Leaf Prints</u>

<u>Materials</u>:
- white paper
- paint
- paint brushes
- differently shaped leaves

<u>Method</u>:

- **Carefully** paint the surface of one of your leaves.

- **Turn** the leaf over and **lay** it down on the paper.

- **Lightly** press it **straight** down, but do not rub or smear.

- **Slowly** peal the leaf off the paper.

- **Repeat** with other leaves to make a pattern or picture.

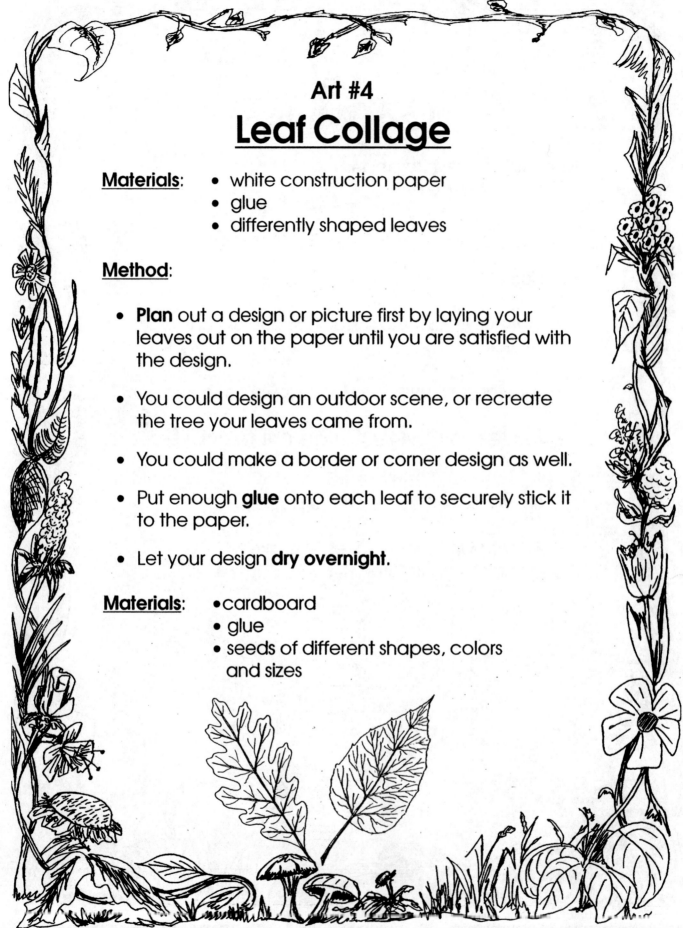

Art #4

Leaf Collage

Materials:
- white construction paper
- glue
- differently shaped leaves

Method:

- **Plan** out a design or picture first by laying your leaves out on the paper until you are satisfied with the design.

- You could design an outdoor scene, or recreate the tree your leaves came from.

- You could make a border or corner design as well.

- Put enough **glue** onto each leaf to securely stick it to the paper.

- Let your design **dry overnight**.

Materials:
- cardboard
- glue
- seeds of different shapes, colors and sizes

Art #5
<u>Seed Picture</u>

<u>Method</u>:

- **Plan** out a design or picture first by laying your seeds out on the paper until you are satisfied with the design.

- You could design an outdoor scene, or make a geometric pattern.

- You could include a border.

- Put enough **glue** onto each seed to securely stick it to the paper.

- Let your design **dry overnight**.

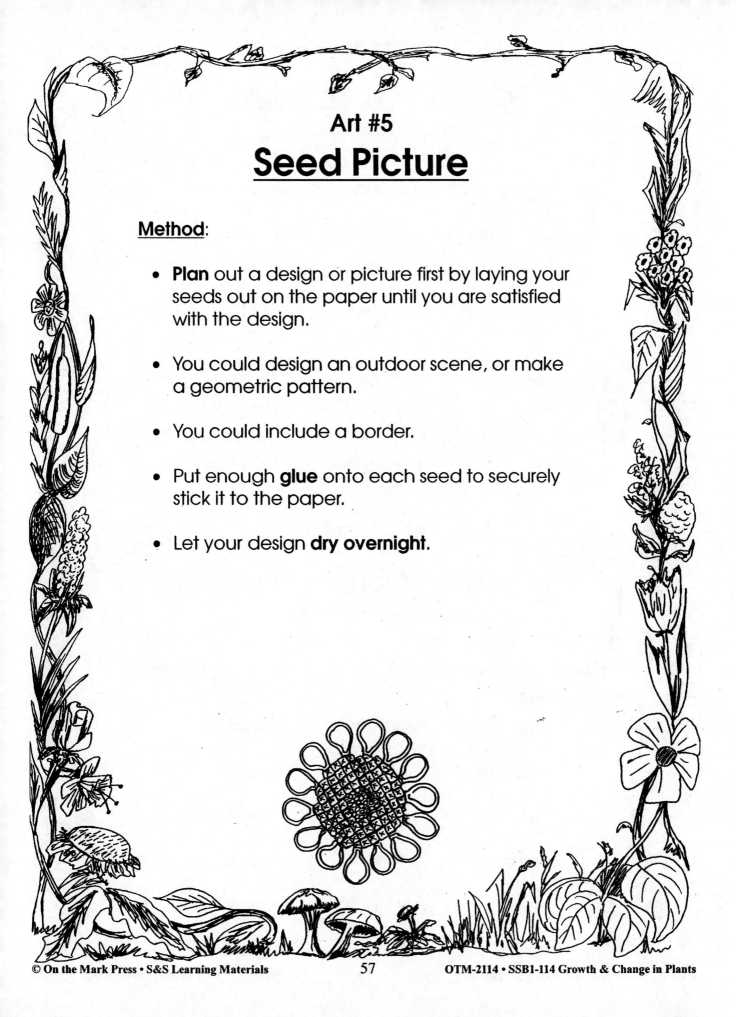

Word Study #1: <u>Syllables</u>

A **syllable** is a group of sounds heard in a word.

<u>Example:</u>   **flower** has 2 syllables   **flow - er**

Copy the following list of words neatly:

Beside each, **print** the **number** of syllables that you hear in each word.

1. dandelion
2. tree
3. buttercup
4. bud

5. pollen
6. branches
7. vine
8. pollinate

9. roots
10. petal
11. annual
12. lichen

Word Study #2: <u>Alphabetical Order</u>

Neatly copy the following list of words in **alphabetical (ABC) order:**

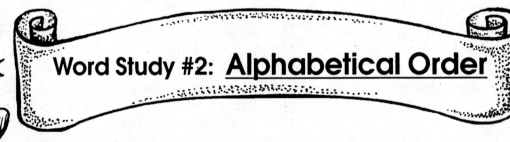

tree	garden	willow
milkweed	weed	sap
fruit	cedar	pussy willow
maple	aspen	tulip
mosses	vegetable	vine
trunk	birch	gardener

Word Study #3: Compound Words

A **compound word** is a word that is made up of two or more little words.

Example: milkweed = milk + weed

Use the words in the word bank to make **compound words**.

Neatly print your new words on your **recording sheet**.

Word Bank

milk, green, snap, nut, mush, mint, house, weed, chest, dog, rag, wood, weed, tumble, room, flower, weed, pepper, sun, dragon

---

Word Study #4: Rhyming Words

Rhyming words sound the same at the end.

Example: **fish - dish**

Copy the list of plant words neatly.

Write a **rhyming** word beside each one.

Try to think of plant words if you can.

1. bean	6. tree
2. vine	7. twig
3. balm	8. bush
4. tansy	9. weed
5. root	10. grain

Word Study #5: <u>Wordsearch</u>

```
A D P C H L O R O P H Y L L J
P H O T O S Y N T H E S I S L
W V L X B I P D F U N G I A K
E O L G A R D E N E R F N R O
N J E H R N P M S R K P G I Y
C M N F K O Z R P W P E I M Q
O K I G W N P E R X I R S V J
P Y G R E E N H O U S E P A L
Y F L O W E R W U P T N E Q H
Y R S H R U B R T L I N Q S N
B U S H N A O E G G L I C E M
K I Q X U F T M Y S T A M E N
M T R E E B A W S O B L X D O
Q W Z P T L N S W E E D C S O
S X E G E C Y F I X S M I I G
```

bark	fruit	photosynthesis	shrub
botany	fungi	pistil	sprout
bush	gardener	pollen	stamen
chlorophyll	greenhouse	seeds	tree
flower	perennial	sepal	weed

Word Study #6: **Crossword**

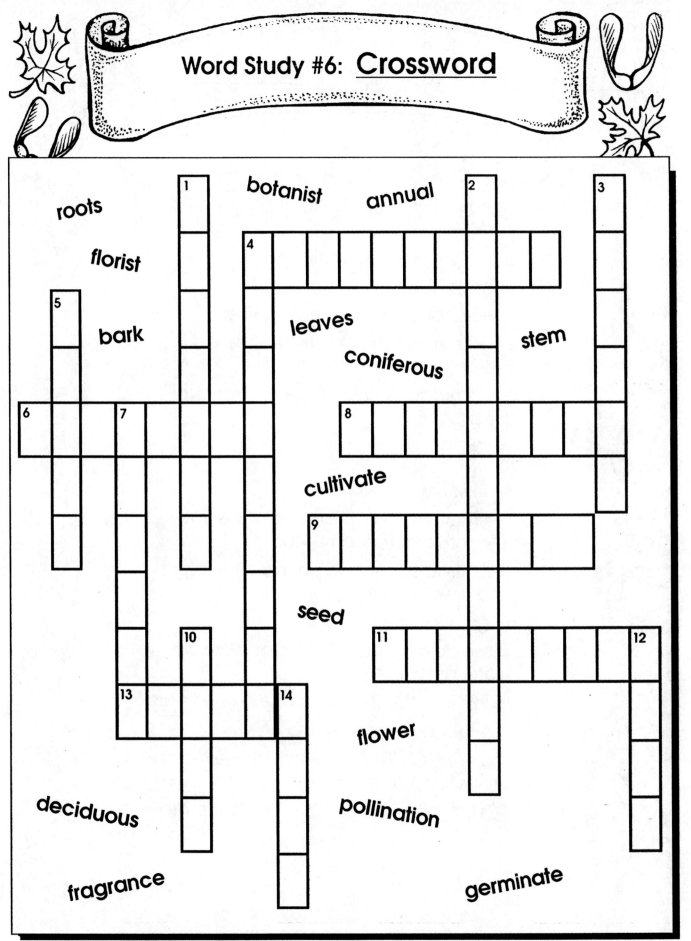

roots

botanist   annual

florist

bark   leaves

stem

coniferous

cultivate

seed

flower

deciduous   pollination

fragrance   germinate

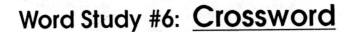

Word Study #6: **Crossword**

Across:

4. Cone-bearing trees that stay green year round.

6. A person who studies plants.

8. To begin to grow.

9. A word for the nice smell of flowers.

11. Trees that lose their leaves in the cold season.

13. These produce chlorophyll and food for the plant.

Down:

1. A person who sells flowers.

2. The movement of pollen from one flower to another of the same kind.

3. This attracts insects to pollinate the plant and create a seed.

4. To grow plants for food.

5. These go down into the soil and absorb water and minerals.

7. Plants that live their life cycle in one year.

10. The tough, outer shell of a tree.

12. This holds up the leaves and flowers and brings food up to them.

14. This has a tiny plant inside it ready to grow.

Word Study #7: Word Endings

Word Endings: s, ed, ing

Copy the chart below.

Rewrite each word with the proper ending.

Watch out for some of the words that change spelling!

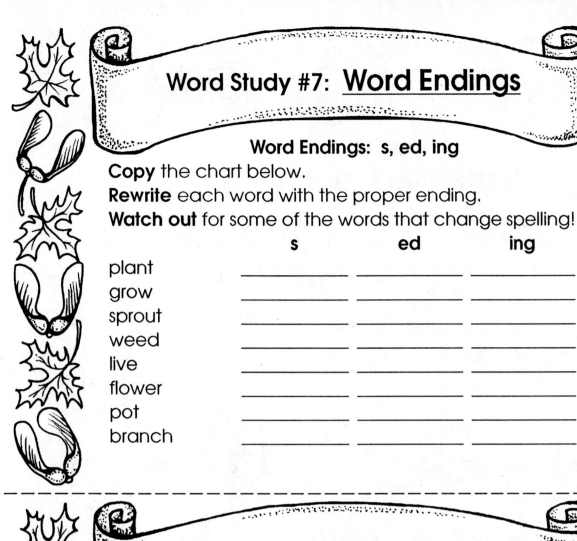

	s	ed	ing
plant			
grow			
sprout			
weed			
live			
flower			
pot			
branch			

Word Study #8: Nouns and Verbs

Nouns are words that are either a **person, place or thing.**

Example: **house**

Verbs are **action** words.

Example: **run**

Make a chart like the example.

Read each word below.

Nouns	Verbs

Neatly print the words in the chart under the correct headings.

Word List:	plant	sprout	harvest
	tree	fertilize	bush
	flower	pollinate	weed

Classification #1
Classifying Leaves - Edges

Leaves come in many shapes and sizes, but they either have **smooth** or **jagged edges**.

In the envelope are some picture cards and title cards.

Sort the leaves according to whether they have **smooth edges** or **jagged edges**.

Classification #2
Classifying Leaves - Simple/Compound

Leaves grow on trees singly or in groups. If they grow alone, they are called **simple leaves**. If they grow in groups they are called **compound leaves**.

In the envelope are some picture cards and title cards.

Sort the leaves according to whether they are **simple** or **compound**.

Classification #1 - Edges: Copy, color and cut out the cards. Mount on a sturdy backing and laminate. Place the cards in an envelope and attach the instruction card. Students will sort the leaf cards under the appropriate headings.

Jagged Edges	Smooth Edges

Ash

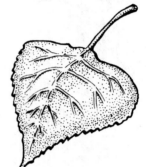

Balsam Poplar

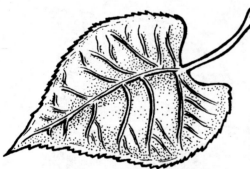

Basswood

Beech

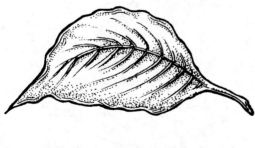

Dogwood

Horse Chestnut

Classification #1 - Edges: Copy, color and cut out the cards. Mount on a sturdy backing and laminate. Place the cards in an envelope and attach the instruction card. Students will sort the leaf cards under the appropriate headings.

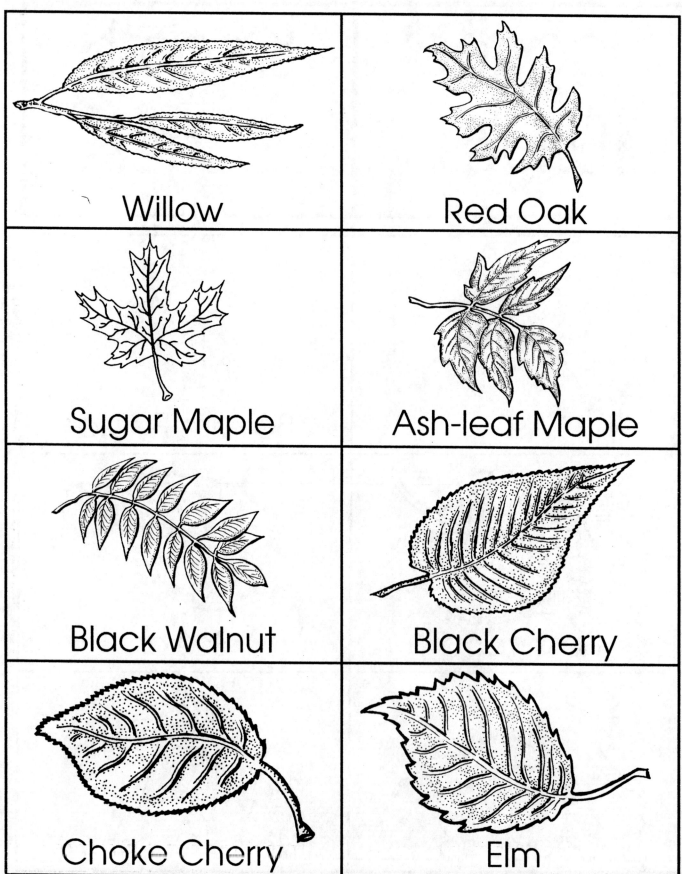

Willow

Red Oak

Sugar Maple

Ash-leaf Maple

Black Walnut

Black Cherry

Choke Cherry

Elm

Classification #2 - Simple/Compound Leaves: Copy, color and cut out the cards. Mount on a sturdy backing and laminate. Place the cards in an envelope and attach the instruction card. Students will sort the leaf cards under the appropriate headings.

Simple Leaves	Compound Leaves

Ash

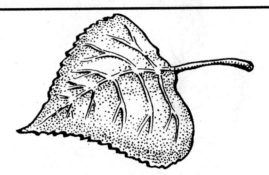

Balsam Poplar

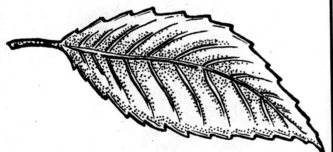

Ironwood

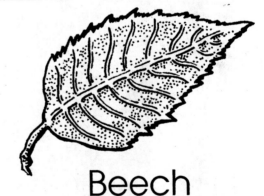

Beech

Dogwood

Horse Chestnut

Classification #2 - Simple/Compound Leaves: Copy, color and cut out the cards. Mount on a sturdy backing and laminate. Place the cards in an envelope and attach the instruction card. Students will sort the leaf cards under the appropriate headings.

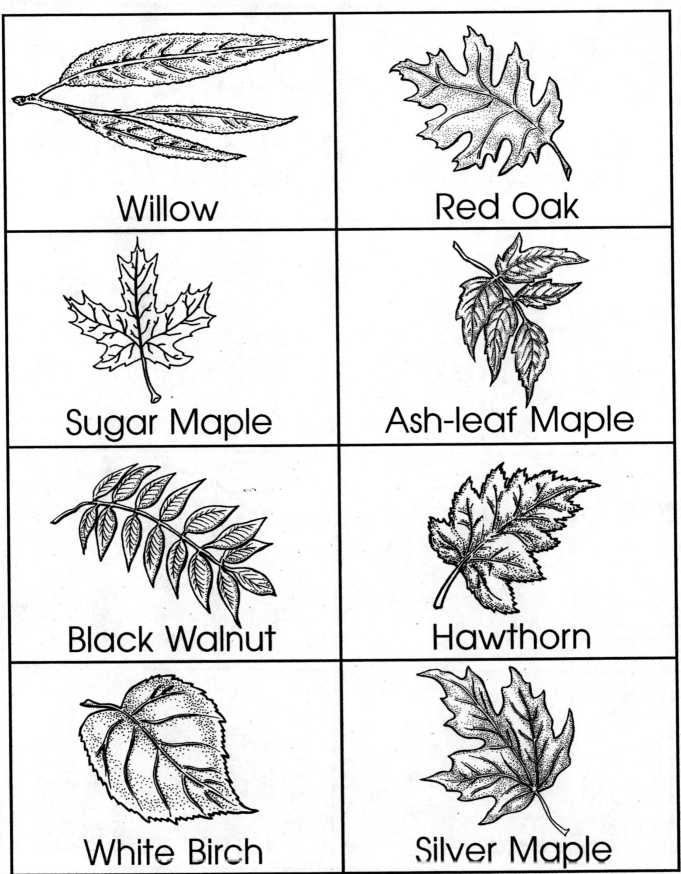

Willow

Red Oak

Sugar Maple

Ash-leaf Maple

Black Walnut

Hawthorn

White Birch

Silver Maple

Classification #3
Classifying Types of Plants

There are many different kinds of plants. Some are trees, some are weeds, some are herbs and some are flowers.

In the **envelope** are some word cards and title cards.

Classify the plants according to whether they are **trees**, **weeds**, **flowers** or **herbs**.

Classification #4
Classifying Edible and Non-Edible Plants

Some plants are used for food and some are not.

In the envelope are some plants words.

Classify them under the proper headings.

Plants We Eat	Plants We Don't Eat
thyme	pine

Classification #3 - Classifying Types of Plants: Copy, color and cut out the cards. Mount on a sturdy backing and laminate. Place the cards in an envelope and attach the instruction card. Students will sort the leaf cards under the appropriate headings.

Trees	Flowers
Weeds	Herbs

maple	oak	basswood
birch	pine	tulip
rose	iris	phlox
snapdragon	thyme	boneset
lavender	rosemary	saffron

burdock	thistle	poison ivy
dandelion	hemlock	poison oak
nettle	milkweed	plantain
beech	willow	palm
daffodil	aster	pansy
daisy	mint	vanilla
fennel	sage	parsley

Classification #4 - Classifying Edible and Non-Edible Plants: Copy, color and cut out the cards. Mount on a sturdy backing and laminate. Place the cards in an envelope and attach the instruction card. Students will sort the leaf cards under the appropriate headings.

Plants We Eat	Plants We Don't Eat

maple	oak	birch
pine	juniper	mint
fennel	willow	basil
lettuce	thyme	bean
carrot	rosemary	potato

Sounds #1

Vowel Combinations

A vowel combination is made of two vowels. The two vowels make one sound.

Example: **tree**

Copy and **complete** the plant words with the correct **vowel combination**.

ee, ea, oo, oa, ou

1. w __ __ d

2. milkw __ __ d

3. redw __ __ d

4. sp __ __ rmint

5. tr __ __

6. spr __ __ t

7. b __ __ n

8. __ __ k

9. gr __ __ nh __ __ se

10. bl __ __ dr __ __ t

Sounds #2

All Kinds of Blends

A **blend** is a sound made by two or three sounds.

Example: **flower**

Copy and **complete** the plant words with the correct **blend**.

bl, dr, fl, fr, gr, pl, pr, sp, st, sn, spr

1. __ __ a __ __ ance
2. __ __ uit
3. __ __ eenhouse
4. __ __ amen
5. __ __ une
6. __ __ icktight
7. __ __ __ out
8. __ __ orist
9. __ __ ant
10. __ __ ossom
11. __ __ ap __ __ agon
12. __ __ __ ing

Sounds #3

Double Consonants

Some words have **double consonants**.

Example: **bunny**

Copy and **complete** the plant words with the correct **double consonant**.

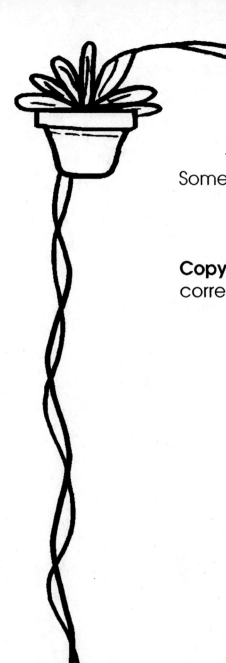

nn, ss, rr, ll, tt, pp, ff

1. da __ __ odil
2. po __ __ y
3. gra __ __
4. be __ __ flower
5. pu __ __ y wi __ __ ow
6. baybe __ __ y
7. vani __ __ a
8. po __ __ en
9. bu __ __ ercup
10. blo __ __ om
11. pere __ __ ial
12. mo __ __

Sounds #4

Long "E"

Some words have a **long "e"** sound. This sound can be spelled in different ways.

<u>Example</u>: **feed, leave**

Copy and **complete** the plant words with the correct spelling of **long "e."**

ee, ea, e

1. l ____ f
2. s ____ pals
3. s ____ d
4. tr ____
5. d ____ ciduous
6. gr ____ nhouse
7. p ____ can
8. coff ____
9. w ____ d
10. t ____ sel
11. tumblew ____ d
12. sp ____ rmint

Sounds #5

Short and Long Vowels

All words have **vowels**. The five vowels are:

$$\boxed{\text{a e i o u}}$$

Sometimes the vowels have a **long** sound as in **cake**.

Sometimes the vowels have a **short** sound as in **cat**.

Copy each word below **neatly**.

Beside each word, **write** whether the vowel sound (or sounds) is **long** or **short**.

1. weed _____
2. moss _____
3. rose _____
4. grass _____
5. petal _____
6. stem _____
7. oak _____
8. seed _____
9. ivy _____
10. sage _____
11. mint _____
12. twig _____

How Seeds Travel

In order to reproduce itself, a plant produces seeds. Some of these seeds will eventually grow into new plants. Seeds travel in different ways.

Research how seeds travel for different plants.

Print the names of at least **two** different plants on the chart that produce seeds that travel in each of the different ways.

By Water	By Air
_____ _____	_____ _____
By Attaching Themselves	**By Exploding**
_____ _____	_____ _____

Seeds or Bulbs?

Research #2

Some plants grow from **seeds** and some grow from **bulbs**.

Look in the library or research center for books on how plants grow.

Print the names of **five** plants on the chart that grow from seeds and **five** that grow from bulbs.

Grow from a Seed	Grow from a Bulb
_____	_____
_____	_____
_____	_____
_____	_____
_____	_____

Terrific Trees

Select a **tree** of your choice to research.

Find out the following information about your tree:

- Where it grows.
- Whether it is coniferous or deciduous.
- What shape its leaves are, whether they are alternating or opposite and whether they are simple or compound.
- How long it lives.
- How tall it gets.
- Any other important information.

Make sure to include drawings of your tree and its leaves.

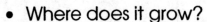

Fantastic Flowers

Choose a flower of your choice.

Research the flower to find out the following things:

- Where does it grow?
- When does it bloom?
- Is it an annual, biennial or perennial?
- Does it produce fruit?
- Does it grow from seeds or from a bulb?
- What type of flower is it?
- What colors does it come in?
- Any other important information.

Illustrate your flower.

Print your information **neatly** in a **booklet**.

Water Plants

Plants grow all over the world. Some even grow in streams, rivers and lakes.

Find out about plants that grow in the water.

Illustrate and **label five** plants on a chart that grow in the water.

Example:

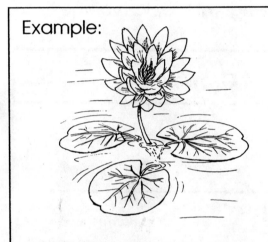

Different Kinds of Trees

Water Plants

There are many different kinds of trees in our world. Some grow only in the hot regions (**tropics**) of the world and some grow in the cooler regions (**temperate.**)

Think of the names of ten trees.

Print each one **neatly** and beside each tell whether it grows in the **tropics** or the **temperate** regions of the world.

Name of Tree	Where it Grows
1. _____	_____
2. _____	_____
3. _____	_____
4. _____	_____
5. _____	_____
6. _____	_____
7. _____	_____
8. _____	_____
9. _____	_____
10. _____	_____

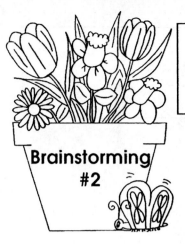

Coniferous and Deciduous Trees

Coniferous trees are trees that bear cones and stay green all year long.

Deciduous trees are trees that lose their leaves during the cold season (winter.)

Think of the names of ten trees.

Decide if they are **coniferous** or **deciduous**.

Write their names **neatly** in the chart below.

Coniferous Trees	Deciduous Trees

Trees as Homes

Some animals use trees as homes.

Think of **six** animals that make their homes in trees.

Illustrate and **label** them below.

Plants Are Useful To Us

Brainstorming #4

Plants are very useful to people. Certain parts can be used to make certain things and some parts of plants can be used by people just as they are.

Think of **six** different ways we can use plants, or parts of plants.

Write each one down neatly.

1. _____

2. _____

3. _____

4. _____

5. _____

6. _____

Colorful Trees

Deciduous trees lose their leaves in the autumn, but first they turn the forests into beautiful colors. Some trees turn yellow, some turn orange and some turn red before turning brown.

Think of things that are **yellow**, **orange**, **red** and **brown**.

Print their names **neatly** in the **chart below**.

Yellow	Orange	Red	Brown

GROWTH and CHANGE in Plants

Answer Key

Reading 1:
1. Trees, bushes and shrubs, mosses, vines and herbaceous plants.
2. Trees are the tallest plants: one thick stem (trunk) and many leaves.
3. Trees are tall and have one stem; bushes are short and have many stems.
4. Perennial means their life cycle takes longer that three years.
5. Mosses grow on rocks, soil, on the bark of trees, in streams and in bogs.
6. Herbs, flowers, grasses, radishes, lettuce, potatoes and gourds.
7. An insectivorous plant traps insects with toothed leaves or sticky liquid.
8. It eats insects.
9. Pitcher plant, bladderwort, Venus's flytrap.

Reading 2:
1. To anchor the plant to the ground and to absorb water and minerals.
2. Roots are also storage areas and food for the plant.
3. Beets, radishes and carrots.
4. Roots store food as starch.
5. Mangrove.
6. Tap roots have one main root growing straight down; fibrous roots have many small roots growing in all directions.
7. Beans, radishes and trees.
8. Corn and grass.

Reading 3:
1. Stems grow leaves and buds.
2. They support the plant, they grow leaves, they provide food storage and they carry water and nutrients.
3. Grow new layers every year which is the outside layer of the stem. This is the layer that brings the food and water up to the leaves.
4. Celery, rhubarb, broccoli, asparagus and sugarcane.

Reading 4:
1. Some leaves are long and thin, while others are broad and round, oval or heart-shaped.
2. They contain chlorophyll.
3. The chlorophyll breaks down and the other colors show through.
4. The food-making process in a leaf or green plant.
5. Leaves breathe out oxygen and pass water vapor back into the air.
6. Lettuce, cabbage, brussel sprouts, mint, basil, dill and rosemary.

Reading 5:
1. They are the reproductive parts of most plants.

GROWTH and CHANGE in Plants

2. The petals are colorful to attract animals and insects that will help pollinate the flower. The scent of a flower also comes from the petals.
3. The anther produces pollen.
4. The pistil is bottle-shaped and has nectar at the top and eggs at the bottom.
5. The eggs are fertilized by the pollen.

Reading 6:
1. Seeds contain the egg that makes a new plant.
2. They may get broken, waterlogged, rotten or eaten by animals.
3. Seeds travel by air, by water, by attaching to animals and clothes, by exploding and by passing through an animal's digestive system.
4. Seeds we eat are sunflower, brazil nuts, coffee, corn, beans, peas and rice.

Reading 7:
1. Most plants grow from seeds.
2. Germination is when a seed begins to grow (sprouts.)
3. Moisture loosens the seed cover.
4. The embryo contains the tiny root, stalk, leaf and bud which will grow the new plant.
5. The plant sends a root down into the soil. A stem starts to grow up.
6. The fruit grows from the flower.
7. A bulb is a mass of leaves surrounding a short stem.
8. Onions, garlic and several flowers such as crocuses, dahlias, tulips, hyacinths, daffodils and gladiolas.

Reading 8:
1. Plants adapt to the seasons and develop defenses against animals and people.
2. Dormancy is a winter sleep.
3. So animals do not eat them.
4. The whole plant can be poisonous or just some parts, such as the berries and leaves.
5. You may get very ill or die.
6. Poison ivy and nettle.

Reading 9:
1. Plants return oxygen, which we need to breathe to the air.
2. Pine, cherry, walnut, oak, teak and mahogany.
3. Tomatoes, cucumbers, pumpkins and melons, and berries such as strawberries, blackberries, blueberries and raspberries.
4. For flavor, teas and medicine.
5. Camomile, hyssop, rose.
6. Borage, digitalis, henbane, primrose, St. John's wort, garlic and camphor.
7. Plants give animals food and shelter.
8. Birds, raccoons, squirrels, chipmunks and other animals build their homes in trees.

GROWTH and CHANGE in Plants

Science 1:
Roots - Bring water and nutrients from the ground.
Leaf Bud - It will grow to be a new leaf.
Stem - Hold up the flowers and the leaves.
Leaf - Make food for the plant.
Seed - It started this plant growing.

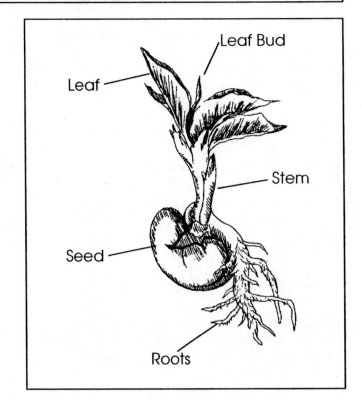

Science 2:
Roots - Brings water and nutrients from the ground.
Bark - Protects the tree from diseases and animals.
Trunk - Holds up the leaves, fruits and seeds.
Leaves - Make food for the tree.
Seeds - Will grow to be new trees.

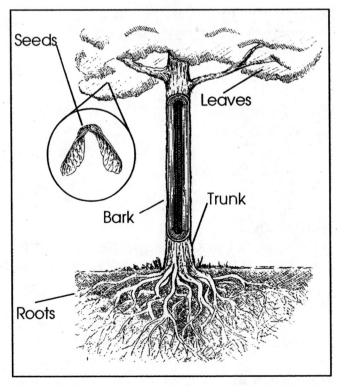

GROWTH and CHANGE in Plants

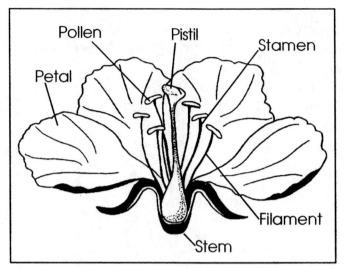

Science 3:
Pistil - seeds develop here.
Stamen - These are found in the flower, they produce pollen.
Pollen - powdery substance used for pollination.
Petal - color attracts birds and insects.
Filament - supports the anther.
Stem - holds up the leaves and the flowers. Carries food and water.

Science 4 - 8:
Answers will vary for experiments.

Science 9:
Answers will vary for experiments. Diagram should look similar to the diagram to the right.

Science 10 - 13:
Answers will vary for experiments.

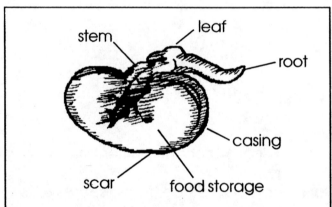

Word Study 1:
1. dandelion - 4
2. tree - 1
3. buttercup - 3
4. bud - 1
5. pollen - 2
6. branches - 2
7. vine - 1
8. pollinate - 3
9. roots - 1
10. petal - 2
11. annual - 3
12. lichen - 2

Word Study 2:
aspen, birch, cedar, fruit, garden, gardener, maple, milkweed, mosses, pussy willow, sap, tulip, tree, trunk, vegetable, vine, weed, willow

Word Study 3:
milkweed, snapdragon, chestnut, dogwood, ragweed, sunflower, peppermint, mushroom, greenhouse, tumbleweed

Word Study 4:
Answers will vary.

GROWTH and CHANGE in Plants

Word Study 5:

```
A D P C H L O R O P H Y L L J
P H O T O S Y N T H E S I S L
W V L X B I P D F U N G I A K
E O L G A R D E N E R F N R O
N J E H R N P M S R K P G I Y
C M N F K O Z R P W P E I M Q
O K I G W N P E R X I R S V J
P Y G R E E N H O U S E P A L
Y F L O W E R W U P T N E Q H
Y R S H R U B R T L I N Q S N
B U S H N A O E G G L I C E M
K I Q X U F T M Y S T A M E N
M T R E E B A W S O B L X D O
Q W Z P T L N S W E E D C S O
S X E G E C Y F I X S M I I G
```

Word Study 6:

Word Study 7:

	s	ed	ing
plant	plants	planted	planting
grow	grows	grew	growing
sprout	sprouts	sprouted	sprouting
weed	weeds	weeded	weeding
live	lives	lived	living
flower	flowers	flowered	flowering
pot	pots	potted	potting
branch	branches	branched	branching

Word Study 8:

Several of these words can be used as both nouns and verbs.

Nouns	Verbs
plant	plant
tree	flower
flower	sprout
sprout	fertilize
bush	pollinate
harvest	harvest
weed	weed

GROWTH and CHANGE in Plants

Classification 1:
Smooth Edges - ash, dogwood, horse chestnut, black cherry
Jagged Edges - basswood, beech, balsam poplar, sugar maple, ash-leaf maple, red oak, willow, black walnut, choke cherry, elm

Classification 2:
Simple Leaves - balsam poplar, ironwood, beech, dogwood, willow, red oak, sugar maple, hawthorn, white birch, silver maple
Compound Leaves - horse chestnut, ash, black walnut, ash-leafed maple

Classification 3:
Trees   - maple, oak, basswood, birch, pine, beech, willow, palm
Flowers - tulip, rose, iris, phlox, snapdragon, daffodil, aster, pansy, daisy
Weeds   - burdock, poison ivy, poison oak, thistle, dandelion, hemlock, nettle, plantain
Herbs   - thyme, boneset, lavender, rosemary, saffron, mint, vanilla, fennel, sage, parsley

Classification 4:
Plants we Eat - mint, fennel, basil, thyme, lettuce, bean, carrot, rosemary, potato
Plants we Don't Eat - maple, oak, birch, pine, juniper, willow

Sounds 1:	Sounds 2:	Sounds 3:	Sounds 4:	Sounds 5:
			12. moss	
1. weed	1. fragrance	1. daffodil	1. leaf	1. long e
2. milkweed	2. fruit	2. poppy	2. sepals	2. short o
3. redwood	3. greenhouse	3. grass	3. seed	3. long o
4. spearmint	4. stamen	4. bellflower	4. tree	4. short a
5. tree	5. prune	5. pussywillow	5. deciduous	5. short e, a
6. sprout	6. sticktight	6. bayberry	6. greenhouse	6. short e
7. bean	7. sprout	7. vanilla	7. pecan	7. long o
8. oak	8. florist	8. pollen	8. coffee	8. long e
9. greenhouse	9. plant	9. buttercup	9. weed	9. long i
10. bloodroot	10. blossom	10. blossom	10. teasel	10. long a
	11. snapdragon	11. perennial	11. tumbleweed	11. short i
	12. spring		12. spearmint	12. short i

Brainstorming 1-5:
Answers will vary.

GROWTH and CHANGE in Plants

Science

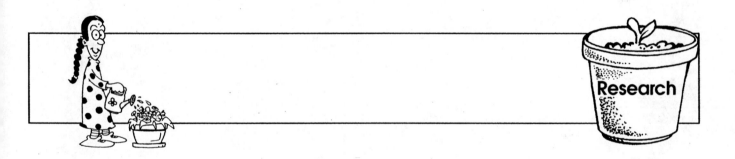

Research

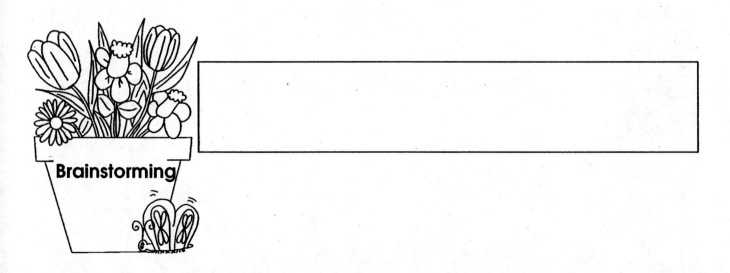

Brainstorming

Publication Listing

See Dealer or
www.sslearning.com
For Pricing
1-800-463-6367

Code #	Title and Grade
SSC1-12	A Time of Plenty Gr. 2
SSN1-92	Abel's Island NS 4-6
SSF1-16	Aboriginal Peoples of Canada Gr. 7-8
SSK1-31	Addition & Subtraction Drills Gr. 1-3
SSK1-28	Addition Drills Gr. 1-3
SSY1-04	Addition Gr. 1-3
SSN1-174	Adv. of Huckle Berry Finn NS 7-8
SSB1-63	African Animals Gr 4-6
SSB1-29	All About Bears Gr. 1-2
SSF1-08	All About Boats Gr. 2-3
SSJ1-02	All About Canada Gr. 2
SSB1-54	All About Cattle Gr. 4-6
SSN1-10	All About Colours Gr. P-1
SSB1-93	All About Dinosaurs Gr. 2
SSN1-14	All About Dragons Gr. 3-5
SSB1-07	All About Elephants Gr. 3-4
SSB1-68	All About Fish Gr. 4-6
SSN1-39	All About Giants Gr. 2-3
SSH1-15	All About Jobs Gr. 1-3
SSH1-05	All About Me Gr. 1
SSA1-02	All About Mexico Gr. 4-6
SSR1-28	All About Nouns Gr. 5-7
SSF1-09	All About Planes Gr. 2-3
SSB1-33	All About Plants Gr. 2-3
SSR1-29	All About Pronouns Gr. 5-7
SSB1-12	All About Rabbits Gr. 2-3
SSB1-58	All About Spiders Gr. 4-6
SSA1-03	All About the Desert Gr. 4-6
SSA1-04	All About the Ocean Gr. 5-7
SSZ1-01	All About the Olympics Gr. 2-4
SSB1-49	All About the Sea Gr. 4-6
SSK1-06	All About Time Gr. 4-6
SSF1-07	All About Trains Gr. 2-3
SSH1-18	All About Transportation Gr. 2
SSB1-01	All About Trees Gr. 4-6
SSB1-61	All About Weather Gr. 7-8
SSB1-06	All About Whales Gr. 3-4
SSPC-26	All Kinds of Clocks B/W Pictures
SSB1-110	All Kinds of Structures Gr. 1
SSH1-19	All Kinds of Vehicles Gr. 3
SSF1-01	Amazing Aztecs Gr. 4-6
SSB1-92	Amazing Earthworms Gr. 2-3
SSJ1-50	Amazing Facts in Cdn History Gr. 4-6
SSB1-32	Amazing Insects Gr. 4-6
SSN1-132	Amelia Bedelia–Camping NS 1-3
SSN1-68	Amelia Bedelia NS 1-3
SSN1-155	Amelia Bedelia-Surprise Shower NS 1-3
SSA1-13	America The Beautiful Gr. 4-6
SSN1-57	Amish Adventure NS 7-8
SSF1-02	Ancient China Gr. 4-6
SSF1-18	Ancient Egypt Gr. 4-6
SSF1-21	Ancient Greece Gr. 4-6
SSF1-19	Ancient Rome Gr. 4-6
SSQ1-06	Animal Town – Big Book Pkg 1-3
SSQ1-02	Animals Prepare Winter- Big Book Pkg 1-3
SSN1-150	Animorphs the Invasion NS 4-6
SSN1-53	Anne of Green Gables NS 7-8
SSB1-40	Apple Celebration Gr. 4-6
SSB1-04	Apple Mania Gr. 2-3
SSB1-38	Apples are the Greatest Gr. P-K
SSB1-59	Arctic Animals Gr. 4-6
SSN1-162	Arnold Lobel Author Study Gr. 2-3
SSPC-22	Australia B/W Pictures
SSA1-05	Australia Gr. 5-8
SSM1-03	Autumn in the Woodlot Gr. 2-3
SSM1-08	Autumn Wonders Gr. 1
SSN1-41	Baby Sister for Frances NS 1-3
SSPC-19	Back to School B/W Pictures
SSC1-33	Back to School Gr. 2-3
SSN1-224	Banner in the Sky NS 7-8
SSN1-36	Bargain for Frances NS 1-3
SSB1-82	Bats Gr. 4-6
SSN1-71	BB – Drug Free Zone NS Gr. 1-3
SSN1-88	BB – In the Freaky House NS 1-3
SSN1-78	BB – Media Madness NS 1-3
SSN1-69	BB – Wheelchair Commando NS 1-3
SSN1-119	Be a Perfect Person-3 Days NS 4-6
SSC1-15	Be My Valentine Gr. 1
SSD1-01	Be Safe Not Sorry Gr. P-1
SSN1-09	Bear Tales Gr. 2-4
SSB1-28	Bears Gr. 4-6
SSN1-202	Bears in Literature Gr. 1-3
SSN1-40	Beatrix Potter Gr. 2-4
SSN1-129	Beatrix Potter: Activity Biography 2-4
SSB1-47	Beautiful Bugs Gr. 1
SSB1-21	Beavers Gr. 3-5
SSN1-257	Because of Winn-Dixie NS Gr. 4-6
SSN1-33	Bedtime for Frances NS 1-3
SSN1-114	Best Christmas Pageant Ever NS 4-6
SSN1-32	Best Friends for Frances NS 1-3
SSB1-39	Best Friends Pets Gr. P-K
SSN1-185	BFG NS Gr. 4-6
SSN1-35	Birthday for Frances NS Gr. 1-3
SSN1-107	Borrowers NS Gr. 4-6
SSC1-16	Bouquet of Valentines Gr. 2
SSN1-29	Bread & Jam for Frances NS 1-3
SSN1-63	Bridge to Terabithia NS Gr. 4-6
SSY1-24	BTS Numeración Gr. 1-3
SSY1-25	BTS Adición Gr. 1-3
SSY1-26	BTS Sustracción Gr. 1-3
SSY1-27	BTS Fonética Gr. 1-3
SSY1-28	BTS Leer para Entender Gr. 1-3
SSY1-29	BTS Uso de las Mayúsculas y Reglas de Puntuación Gr. 1-3
SSY1-30	BTS Composición de Oraciones Gr. 1-3
SSY1-31	BTS Composici13n de Historias Gr. 1-3
SSN1-256	Bud, Not Buddy NS Gr. 4-6
SSB1-31	Bugs, Bugs & More Bugs Gr. 2-3
SSR1-07	Building Word Families L.V. 1-2
SSR1-05	Building Word Families S.V. 1-2
SSN1-204	Bunnicula NS Gr. 4-6
SSB1-80	Butterflies & Caterpillars Gr. 1-2
SSN1-164	Call It Courage NS Gr. 7-8
SSN1-67	Call of the Wild NS Gr. 7-8
SSJ1-41	Canada & It's Trading Partners 6-8
SSPC-28	Canada B/W Pictures
SSN1-173	Canada Geese Quilt NS Gr. 4-6
SSJ1-01	Canada Gr. 1
SSJ1-33	Canada's Capital Cities Gr. 4-6
SSJ1-43	Canada's Confederation Gr. 7-8
SSF1-04	Canada's First Nations Gr. 7-8
SSJ1-51	Canada's Landmarks Gr. 1-3
SSJ1-48	Canada's Landmarks Gr. 4-6
SSJ1-42	Canada's Traditions & Celeb. Gr. 1-3
SSB1-45	Canadian Animals Gr. 1-2
SSJ1-37	Canadian Arctic Inuit Gr. 2-3
SSJ1-53	Canadian Black History Gr. 4-8
SSJ1-57	Canadian Comprehension Gr. 1-2
SSJ1-58	Canadian Comprehension Gr. 3-4
SSJ1-59	Canadian Comprehension Gr. 5-6
SSJ1-46	Canadian Industries Gr. 4-6
SSK1-12	Canadian Problem Solving Gr. 4-6
SSJ1-38	Canadian Provinces & Terr. Gr. 4-6
SSY1-07	Capitalization & Punctuation Gr. 1-3
SSN1-198	Captain Courageous NS Gr. 7-8
SSK1-11	Cars Problem Solving Gr. 3-4
SSN1-154	Castle in the Attic NS Gr. 4-6
SSF1-31	Castles & Kings Gr. 4-6
SSN1-144	Cat Ate My Gymsuit NS Gr. 4-6
SSPC-38	Cats B/W Pictures
SSB1-50	Cats – Domestic & Wild Gr. 4-6
SSN1-34	Cats in Literature Gr. 3-6
SSN1-212	Cay NS Gr. 7-8
SSM1-09	Celebrate Autumn Gr. 4-6
SSC1-39	Celebrate Christmas Gr. 4-6
SSC1-31	Celebrate Easter Gr. 4-6
SSC1-23	Celebrate Shamrock Day Gr. 2
SSM1-11	Celebrate Spring Gr. 4-6
SSC1-13	Celebrate Thanksgiving R. 3-4
SSM1-06	Celebrate Winter Gr. 4-6
SSB1-107	Cells, Tissues & Organs Gr. 7-8
SSB1-101	Characteristics of Flight Gr. 4-6
SSN1-66	Charlie & Chocolate Factory NS 4-6
SSN1-23	Charlotte's Web NS Gr. 4-6
SSB1-37	Chicks N'Ducks Gr. 2-4
SSA1-09	China Today Gr. 5-8
SSN1-70	Chocolate Fever NS Gr. 4-6
SSN1-241	Chocolate Touch NS Gr. 4-6
SSC1-38	Christmas Around the World Gr. 4-6
SSPC-42	Christmas B/W Pictures
SST1-08A	Christmas Gr. JK/SK
SST1-08B	Christmas Gr. 1
SST1-08C	Christmas Gr. 2-3
SSC1-04	Christmas Magic Gr. 1
SSC1-03	Christmas Tales Gr. 2-3
SSG1-06	Cinematography Gr. 5-8
SSPC-13	Circus B/W Pictures
SSF1-03	Circus Magic Gr. 3-4
SSJ1-52	Citizenship/Immigration Gr. 4-8
SSN1-104	Classical Poetry Gr. 7-12
SSN1-227	Color Gr. 1-3
SSN1-203	Colour Gr. 1-3
SSN1-135	Come Back Amelia Bedelia NS 1-3
SSH1-11	Community Helpers Gr. 1-3
SSK1-02	Concept Cards & Activities Gr. P-1
SSN1-183	Copper Sunrise NS Gr. 7-8
SSN1-86	Corduroy & Pocket Corduroy NS 1-3
SSN1-124	Could Dracula Live in Wood NS 4-6
SSN1-148	Cowboy's Don't Cry NS Gr. 7-8
SSR1-01	Creativity with Food Gr. 4-8
SSB1-34	Creatures of the Sea Gr. 2-4
SSN1-208	Curse of the Viking Grave NS 7-8
SSN1-134	Danny Champion of World NS 4-6
SSN1-98	Danny's Run NS Gr. 7-8
SSK1-21	Data Management Gr. 4-6
SSB1-53	Dealing with Dinosaurs Gr. 4-6
SSN1-178	Dear Mr. Henshaw NS Gr. 4-6
SSB1-22	Deer Gr. 3-5
SSPC-20	Desert B/W Pictures
SSJ1-40	Development of Western Canada 7-8
SSA1-16	Development of Manufacturing 7-9
SSN1-105	Dicken's Christmas NS Gr. 7-8
SSN1-62	Different Dragons NS Gr. 4-6
SSPC-21	Dinosaurs B/W Pictures
SSB1-16	Dinosaurs Gr. 1
SST1-02A	Dinosaurs Gr. JK/SK
SST1-02B	Dinosaurs Gr. 1
SST1-02 C	Dinosaurs Gr. 2-3
SSN1-175	Dinosaurs in Literature Gr. 1-3
SSJ1-26	Discover Nova Scotia Gr. 5-7
SSJ1-36	Discover Nunavut Territory Gr. 5-7
SSJ1-25	Discover Ontario Gr. 5-7
SSJ1-24	Discover PEI Gr. 5-7
SSJ1-22	Discover Québec Gr. 5-7
SSL1-01	Discovering the Library Gr. 2-3
SSB1-106	Diversity of Living Things Gr. 4-6
SSK1-27	Division Drills Gr. 4-6
SSB1-30	Dogs – Wild & Tame Gr. 4-6
SSPC-31	Dogs B/W Pictures
SSN1-196	Dog's Don't Tell Jokes NS Gr. 4-6
SSN1-182	Door in the Wall NS Gr. 4-6
SSB1-87	Down by the Sea Gr. 1-3
SSN1-189	Dr. Jeckyll & Mr. Hyde NS Gr. 4-6
SSG1-07	Dragon Trivia Gr. P-8
SSN1-102	Dragon's Egg NS Gr. 4-6
SSN1-16	Dragons in Literature Gr. 3-6
SSC1-06	Early Christmas Gr. 3-5
SSB1-109	Earth's Crust Gr. 6-8
SSC1-21	Easter Adventures Gr. 3-4
SSC1-17	Easter Delights Gr. P-K
SSC1-19	Easter Surprises Gr. 1
SSPC-12	Egypt B/W Pictures
SSN1-255	Egypt Game NS Gr. 4-6
SSF1-28	Egyptians Today & Yesterday Gr. 2-3
SSJ1-49	Elections in Canada Gr. 4-8
SSB1-108	Electricity Gr. 4-6
SSN1-02	Elves & the Shoemaker NS Gr. 1-3
SSH1-14	Emotions Gr. P-2
SSB1-85	Energy Gr. 4-6
SSN1-108	English Language Gr. 10-12
SSN1-156	Enjoying Eric Wilson Series Gr. 5-7
SSB1-64	Environment Gr. 4-6
SSR1-12	ESL Teaching Ideas Gr. K-8
SSN1-258	Esperanza Rising NS Gr. 4-6
SSR1-22	Exercises in Grammar Gr. 6
SSR1-23	Exercises in Grammar Gr. 7
SSR1-24	Exercises in Grammar Gr. 8
SSF1-20	Exploration Gr. 4-6
SSF1-15	Explorers & Mapmakers of Can. 7-8
SSJ1-54	Exploring Canada Gr. 1-3
SSJ1-56	Exploring Canada Gr. 1-6
SSJ1-55	Exploring Canada Gr. 4-6
SSH1-20	Exploring My School & Community 1
SSPC-39	Fables B/W Pictures
SSN1-15	Fables Gr. 4-6
SSN1-04	Fairy Tale Magic Gr. 3-5
SSPC-11	Fairy Tales B/W Pictures
SSN1-11	Fairy Tales Gr. 1-2
SSN1-199	Family Under the Bridge NS 4-6
SSPC-41	Famous Canadians B/W Pictures
SSJ1-12	Famous Canadians Gr. 4-8
SSN1-210	Fantastic Mr. Fox NS Gr. 4-6
SSB1-36	Fantastic Plants Gr. 4-6
SSPC-04	Farm Animals B/W Pictures
SSB1-15	Farm Animals Gr. 1-2
SST1-03A	Farm Gr. JK/SK
SST1-03B	Farm Gr. 1
SST1-03C	Farm Gr. 2-3
SSJ1-05	Farming Community Gr. 3-4
SSB1-44	Farmyard Friends Gr. P-K
SSJ1-45	Fathers of Confederation Gr. 4-8
SSB1-19	Feathered Friends Gr. 4-6
SST1-05A	February Gr. JK/SK
SST1-05B	February Gr. 1
SST1-05C	February Gr. 2-3
SSN1-03	Festival of Fairytales Gr. 3-5
SSC1-36	Festivals Around the World Gr. 2-3
SSN1-168	First 100 Sight Words Gr. 1
SSC1-32	First Days at School Gr. 1
SSJ1-06	Fishing Community Gr. 3-4
SSN1-170	Flowers for Algernon NS Gr. 7-8
SSN1-128	Fly Away Home NS Gr. 4-6
SSD1-05	Food: Fact, Fun & Fiction Gr. 1-3
SSD1-06	Food: Nutrition & Invention Gr. 4-6
SSB1-118	Force and Motion Gr. 1-3
SSB1-119	Force and Motion Gr. 4-6
SSB1-25	Foxes Gr. 3-5
SSN1-172	Freckle Juice NS Gr. 1-3
SSB1-43	Friendly Frogs Gr. 1
SSB1-89	Fruits & Seeds Gr. 4-6
SSN1-137	Fudge-a-Mania NS Gr. 4-6
SSB1-14	Fun on the Farm Gr. 3-4
SSR1-49	Fun with Phonics Gr. 1-3
SSPC-06	Garden Flowers B/W Pictures
SSK1-03	Geometric Shapes Gr. 2-5
SSC1-18	Get the Rabbit Habit Gr. 1-2
SSN1-209	Giver, The NS Gr. 7-8
SSN1-190	Go Jump in the Pool NS Gr. 4-6
SSG1-03	Goal Setting Gr. 6-8
SSG1-08	Gr. 3 Test – Parent Guide
SSG1-99	Gr. 3 Test – Teacher Guide
SSG1-09	Gr. 6 Language Test–Parent Guide
SSG1-97	Gr. 6 Language Test–Teacher Guide
SSG1-10	Gr. 6 Math Test – Parent Guide
SSG1-96	Gr. 6 Math Test – Teacher Guide
SSG1-98	Gr. 6 Math/Lang. Test–Teacher Guide
SSK1-14	Graph for all Seasons Gr. 1-3
SSN1-117	Great Brain NS Gr. 4-6
SSN1-90	Great Expectations NS Gr. 7-8
SSN1-169	Great Gilly Hopkins NS Gr. 4-6
SSN1-197	Great Science Fair Disaster NS 4-6
SSN1-138	Greek Mythology Gr. 7-8
SSN1-113	Green Gables Detectives NS 4-6
SSC1-26	Groundhog Celebration Gr. 2
SSC1-25	Groundhog Day Gr. 1
SSB1-113	Growth & Change in Animals Gr. 2-3
SSB1-114	Growth & Change in Plants Gr. 2-3
SSB1-48	Guinea Pigs & Friends Gr. 3-5
SSB1-104	Habitats Gr. 4-6
SSPC-18	Halloween B/W Pictures
SST1-04A	Halloween Gr. JK/SK
SST1-04B	Halloween Gr. 1
SST1-04C	Halloween Gr. 2-3
SSC1-10	Halloween Gr. 4-6
SSC1-08	Halloween Happiness Gr. 1
SSC1-29	Halloween Spirits Gr. P-K
SSC1-42	Happy Valentines Day Gr. 3
SSN1-205	Harper Moon NS Gr. 7-8
SSN1-123	Harriet the Spy NS Gr. 4-6
SSC1-11	Harvest Time Wonders Gr. 1
SSN1-136	Hatchet NS Gr. 7-8
SSC1-09	Haunting Halloween Gr. 2-3
SSN1-91	Hawk & Stretch NS Gr. 4-6
SSC1-30	Hearts & Flowers Gr. P-K
SSN1-22	Heidi NS Gr. 4-6
SSN1-120	Help I'm Trapped in My NS 4-6
SSN1-24	Henry & the Clubhouse NS 4-6
SSN1-184	Hobbit NS Gr. 7-8
SSN1-122	Hoboken Chicken Emerg. NS 4-6
SSN1-250	Holes NS Gr. 4-6
SSN1-116	How Can a Frozen Detective NS 4-6
SSN1-89	How Can I be a Detective if I NS 4-6
SSN1-96	How Come the Best Clues... NS 4-6
SSN1-133	How To Eat Fried Worms NS 4-6
SSR1-48	How To Give a Presentation Gr. 4-6
SSN1-125	How To Teach Writing Through 7-9
SSR1-10	How To Write a Composition 6-10
SSR1-09	How To Write a Paragraph 5-10
SSR1-08	How To Write an Essay Gr. 7-12
SSR1-03	How To Write Poetry & Stories 4-6
SSD1-07	Human Body Gr. 2-4
SSD1-02	Human Body Gr. 4-6
SSN1-25	I Want to Go Home NS Gr. 4-6
SSH1-06	I'm Important Gr. 2-3
SSH1-07	I'm Unique Gr. 4-6
SSF1-05	In Days of Yore Gr. 4-6
SSF1-06	In Pioneer Days Gr. 2-4
SSM1-10	In the Wintertime Gr. 2
SSB1-41	Incredible Dinosaurs Gr. P-1
SSN1-177	Incredible Journey NS Gr. 4-6
SSN1-100	Indian in the Cupboard NS Gr. 4-6
SSPC-05	Insects B/W Pictures
SSPC-10	Inuit B/W Pictures

Publication Listing

Code #	Title and Grade
SSJ1-10	Inuit Community Gr. 3-4
SSN1-85	Ira Sleeps Over NS Gr. 1-3
SSN1-93	Iron Man NS Gr. 4-6
SSN1-193	Island of the Blue Dolphins NS 4-6
SSB1-11	It's a Dogs World Gr. 2-3
SSM1-05	It's a Marshmallow World Gr. 3
SSK1-05	It's About Time Gr. 2-4
SSC1-41	It's Christmas Time Gr. 3
SSH1-04	It's Circus Time Gr. 1
SSC1-43	It's Groundhog Day Gr. 3
SSB1-75	It's Maple Syrup Time Gr. 2-4
SSC1-40	It's Trick or Treat Time Gr. 2
SSN1-65	James & The Giant Peach NS 4-6
SSN1-106	Jane Eyre NS Gr. 7-8
SSPC-25	Japan B/W Pictures
SSA1-06	Japan Gr. 5-8
SSC1-05	Joy of Christmas Gr. 2
SSN1-161	Julie of the Wolves NS Gr. 7-8
SSB1-81	Jungles Gr. 2-3
SSE1-02	Junior Music for Fall Gr. 4-6
SSE1-05	Junior Music for Spring Gr. 4-6
SSE1-06	Junior Music for Winter Gr. 4-6
SSN1-151	Kate NS Gr. 4-6
SSN1-95	Kidnapped in the Yukon NS Gr. 4-6
SSN1-140	Kids at Bailey School Gr. 2-4
SSN1-176	King of the Wind NS Gr. 4-6
SSF1-29	Klondike Gold Rush Gr. 4-6
SSF1-33	Labour Movement in Canada Gr. 7-8
SSN1-152	Lamplighter NS Gr. 4-6
SSB1-98	Learning About Dinosaurs Gr. 3
SSN1-38	Learning About Giants Gr. 4-6
SSK1-22	Learning About Measurement Gr. 1-3
SSB1-46	Learning About Mice Gr. 3-5
SSK1-09	Learning About Money CDN Gr. 1-3
SSK1-19	Learning About Money USA Gr. 1-3
SSK1-23	Learning About Numbers Gr. 1-3
SSB1-69	Learning About Rocks & Soils Gr. 2-3
SSK1-08	Learning About Shapes Gr. 1-3
SSB1-100	Learning About Simple Machines 1-3
SSK1-04	Learning About the Calendar Gr. 2-3
SSK1-10	Learning About Time Gr. 1-3
SSH1-17	Learning About Transportation Gr. 1
SSB1-02	Leaves Gr. 2-3
SSN1-50	Legends Gr. 4-6
SSC1-27	Lest We Forget Gr. 4-6
SSJ1-13	Let's Look at Canada Gr. 4-6
SSJ1-16	Let's Visit Alberta Gr. 2-4
SSJ1-15	Let's Visit British Columbia Gr. 2-4
SSJ1-03	Let's Visit Canada Gr. 3
SSJ1-18	Let's Visit Manitoba Gr. 2-4
SSJ1-21	Let's Visit New Brunswick Gr. 2-4
SSJ1-27	Let's Visit NFLD & Labrador Gr. 2-4
SSJ1-30	Let's Visit North West Terr. Gr. 2-4
SSJ1-20	Let's Visit Nova Scotia Gr. 2-4
SSJ1-34	Let's Visit Nunavut Gr. 2-4
SSJ1-17	Let's Visit Ontario Gr. 2-4
SSQ1-08	Let's Visit Ottawa Big Book Pkg 1-3
SSJ1-19	Let's Visit PEI Gr. 2-4
SSJ1-31	Let's Visit Québec Gr. 2-4
SSJ1-14	Let's Visit Saskatchewan Gr. 2-4
SSJ1-28	Let's Visit Yukon Gr. 2-4
SSN1-130	Life & Adv. of Santa Claus NS 7-8
SSB1-10	Life in a Pond Gr. 3-4
SSF1-30	Life in the Middle Ages Gr. 7-8
SSB1-103	Light & Sound Gr. 4-6
SSN1-219	Light in the Forest NS Gr. 7-8
SSN1-121	Light on Hogback Hill NS Gr. 4-6
SSN1-46	Lion, Witch & the Wardrobe NS 4-6
SSR1-51	Literature Response Forms Gr. 1-3
SSR1-52	Literature Response Forms Gr. 4-6
SSN1-28	Little House Big Woods NS 4-6
SSN1-233	Little House on the Prairie NS 4-6
SSN1-111	Little Women NS Gr. 7-8
SSN1-115	Live from the Fifth Grade NS 4-6
SSN1-141	Look Through My Window NS 4-6
SSN1-112	Look! Visual Discrimination Gr. P-1
SSN1-61	Lost & Found NS Gr. 4-6
SSN1-109	Lost in the Barrens NS Gr. 7-8
SSJ1-08	Lumbering Community Gr. 3-4
SSN1-167	Magic School Bus Gr. 1-3
SSN1-247	Magic Treehouse Gr. 1-3
SSB1-78	Magnets Gr. 3-5
SSD1-03	Making Sense of Our Senses K-1
SSN1-146	Mama's Going to Buy You a NS 4-6
SSB1-94	Mammals Gr. 1
SSB1-95	Mammals Gr. 2
SSB1-96	Mammals Gr. 3
SSB1-97	Mammals Gr. 5-6
SSN1-160	Maniac Magee NS Gr. 4-6
SSA1-19	Mapping Activities & Outlines! 4-8
SSA1-17	Mapping Skills Gr. 1-3

Code #	Title and Grade
SSA1-07	Mapping Skills Gr. 4-6
SST1-10A	March Gr. JK/SK
SST1-10B	March Gr. 1
SST1-10C	March Gr. 2-3
SSB1-57	Marvellous Marsupials Gr. 4-6
SSK1-01	Math Signs & Symbols Gr. 1-3
SSB1-116	Matter & Materials Gr. 1-3
SSB1-117	Matter & Materials Gr. 4-6
SSH1-03	Me, I'm Special! Gr. P-1
SSK1-16	Measurement Gr. 4-8
SSC1-02	Medieval Christmas Gr. 4-6
SSPC-09	Medieval Life B/W Pictures
SSC1-07	Merry Christmas Gr. P-K
SSK1-15	Metric Measurement Gr. 4-8
SSN1-13	Mice in Literature Gr. 3-5
SSB1-70	Microscopy Gr. 4-6
SSN1-180	Midnight Fox NS Gr. 4-6
SSN1-243	Midwife's Apprentice NS Gr. 4-6
SSJ1-07	Mining Community Gr. 3-4
SSK1-17	Money Talks – Cdn Gr. 3-6
SSK1-18	Money Talks – USA Gr. 3-6
SSB1-56	Monkeys & Apes Gr. 4-6
SSN1-43	Monkeys in Literature Gr. 2-4
SSN1-54	Monster Mania Gr. 4-6
SSN1-97	Mouse & the Motorcycle NS 4-6
SSN1-94	Mr. Poppers Penguins NS Gr. 4-6
SSN1-201	Mrs. Frisby & Rats NS Gr. 4-6
SSR1-13	Milti-Level Spelling Program Gr. 3-6
SSR1-26	Multi-Level Spelling USA Gr. 3-6
SSK1-31	Addition & Subtraction Drills 1-3
SSK1-32	Multiplication & Division Drills 4-6
SSK1-30	Multiplication Drills Gr. 4-6
SSA1-14	My Country! The USA! Gr. 2-4
SSN1-186	My Side of the Mountain NS 7-8
SSN1-58	Mysteries, Monsters & Magic Gr. 6-8
SSN1-37	Mystery at Blackrock Island NS 7-8
SSN1-80	Mystery House NS 4-6
SSN1-157	Nate the Great & Sticky Case NS 1-3
SSF1-23	Native People of North America 4-6
SSF1-25	New France Part 1 Gr. 7-8
SSF1-27	New France Part 2 Gr. 7-8
SSA1-10	New Zealand Gr. 4-8
SSN1-51	Newspapers Gr. 5-8
SSN1-47	No Word for Goodbye NS Gr. 7-8
SSPC-03	North American Animals B/W Pictures
SSF1-22	North American Natives Gr. 2-4
SSN1-75	Novel Ideas Gr. 4-6
SST1-06A	November JK/SK
SST1-06B	November Gr. 1
SST1-06C	November Gr. 2-3
SSN1-244	Number the Stars NS Gr. 4-6
SSY1-03	Numeration Gr. 1-3
SSPC-14	Nursery Rhymes B/W Pictures
SSN1-12	Nursery Rhymes Gr. P-1
SSN1-59	On the Banks of Plum Creek NS 4-6
SSN1-220	One in Middle Green Kangaroo NS 1-3
SSN1-145	One to Grow On NS Gr. 4-6
SSB1-27	Opossums Gr. 3-5
SSJ1-23	Ottawa Gr. 7-9
SSJ1-39	Our Canadian Governments Gr. 5-8
SSF1-14	Our Global Heritage Gr. 4-6
SSH1-12	Our Neighbourhoods Gr. 4-6
SSB1-72	Our Trash Gr. 2-3
SSB1-51	Our Universe Gr. 5-8
SSB1-86	Outer Space Gr. 1-2
SSA1-18	Outline Maps of the World Gr. 1-8
SSB1-67	Owls Gr. 4-6
SSN1-31	Owls in the Family NS Gr. 4-6
SSL1-02	Oxbridge Owl & The Library Gr. 4-6
SSB1-71	Pandas, Polar & Penguins Gr. 4-6
SSN1-52	Paperbag Princess NS Gr. 1-3
SSR1-11	Passion of Jesus: A Play Gr. 7-8
SSA1-12	Passport to Adventure Gr. 4-5
SSR1-06	Passport to Adventure Gr. 7-8
SSR1-04	Personal Spelling Dictionary Gr. 2-5
SSPC-29	Pets B/W Pictures
SSE1-03	Phantom of the Opera Gr. 7-9
SSN1-171	Phoebe Gilman Author Study Gr. 2-3
SSY1-06	Phonics Gr. 1-3
SSN1-237	Pierre Berton Author Study Gr. 7-8
SSN1-179	Pigman NS Gr. 7-8
SSN1-48	Pigs in Literature Gr. 2-4
SSN1-99	Pinballs NS Gr. 4-6
SSN1-60	Pippi Longstocking NS Gr. 4-6
SSF1-12	Pirates Gr. 4-6
SSK1-13	Place Value Gr. 4-6
SSB1-77	Planets Gr. 3-6
SSR1-74	Poetry Prompts Gr. 1-3
SSR1-75	Poetry Prompts Gr. 4-6
SSB1-66	Popcorn Fun Gr. 2-3
SSB1-20	Porcupines Gr. 3-5
SSF1-24	Prehistoric Times Gr. 4-6

Code #	Title and Grade
SSE1-01	Primary Music for Fall Gr. 1-3
SSE1-04	Primary Music for Spring Gr. 1-3
SSE1-07	Primary Music for Winter Gr. 1-3
SSJ1-47	Prime Ministers of Canada Gr. 4-8
SSK1-20	Probability & Inheritance Gr. 7-10
SSN1-49	Question of Loyalty NS Gr. 7-8
SSN1-26	Rabbits in Literature Gr. 2-4
SSB1-17	Raccoons Gr. 3-5
SSN1-207	Radio Fifth Grade NS Gr. 4-6
SSB1-52	Rainbow of Colours Gr. 4-6
SSN1-144	Ramona Quimby Age 8 NS 4-6
SSJ1-09	Ranching Community Gr. 3-4
SSY1-08	Reading for Meaning Gr. 1-3
SSN1-165	Reading Response Forms Gr. 1-3
SSN1-239	Reading Response Forms Gr. 4-6
SSN1-234	Reading with Arthur Gr. 1-3
SSN1-249	Reading with Canadian Authors 1-3
SSN1-200	Reading with Curious George Gr. 2-4
SSN1-230	Reading with Eric Carle Gr. 1-3
SSN1-251	Reading with Kenneth Oppel Gr. 4-6
SSN1-127	Reading with Mercer Mayer Gr. 1-2
SSN1-07	Reading with Motley Crew Gr. 2-3
SSN1-142	Reading with Robert Munsch 1-3
SSN1-06	Reading with the Super Sleuths 4-6
SSN1-08	Reading with the Ziggles Gr. 1
SST1-11A	Red Gr. JK/SK
SSN1-147	Refuge NS Gr. 7-8
SSC1-44	Remembrance Day Gr. 1-3
SSPC-23	Reptiles B/W Pictures
SSB1-42	Reptiles Gr. 4-6
SSN1-110	Return of the Indian NS Gr. 4-6
SSN1-225	River NS Gr. 7-8
SSE1-08	Robert Schuman, Composer Gr. 6-9
SSN1-83	Robot Alert NS Gr. 4-6
SSB1-65	Rocks & Minerals Gr. 4-6
SSN1-149	Romeo & Juliet NS Gr. 7-8
SSB1-88	Romping Reindeer Gr. K-3
SSN1-21	Rumplestiltskin NS Gr. 1-3
SSN1-153	Runaway Ralph NS Gr. 4-6
SSN1-103	Sadako & 1000 Paper Cranes NS 4-6
SSD1-04	Safety Gr. 2-4
SSN1-42	Sarah Plain & Tall NS Gr. 4-6
SSC1-34	School in September Gr. 4-6
SSPC-01	Sea Creatures B/W Pictures
SSB1-79	Sea Creatures Gr. 1-3
SSN1-64	Secret Garden NS Gr. 4-6
SSB1-90	Seeds & Weeds Gr. 2-3
SSY1-02	Sentence Writing Gr. 1-3
SST1-07A	September JK/SK
SST1-07B	September Gr. 1
SST1-07C	September Gr. 2-3
SSN1-30	Serendipity Series Gr. 3-5
SSC1-22	Shamrocks on Parade Gr. 1
SSC1-24	Shamrocks, Harps & Shillelaghs 3-4
SSR1-66	Shakespeare Shorts-Perf Arts Gr. 1-4
SSR1-67	Shakespeare Shorts-Perf Arts Gr. 4-6
SSR1-68	Shakespeare Shorts-Lang Arts Gr. 2-4
SSR1-69	Shakespeare Shorts-Lang Arts Gr. 4-6
SSB1-74	Sharks Gr. 4-6
SSN1-158	Shiloh NS Gr. 4-6
SSN1-84	Sideways Stories Wayside NS 4-6
SSN1-181	Sight Words Activities Gr. 1
SSB1-99	Simple Machines Gr. 4-6
SSN1-19	Sixth Grade Secrets 4-6
SSG1-04	Skill Building with Slates Gr. K-8
SSN1-118	Skinny Bones NS Gr. 4-6
SSB1-24	Skunks Gr. 3-5
SSN1-191	Sky is Falling NS Gr. 4-6
SSB1-83	Slugs & Snails Gr. 1-3
SSB1-55	Snakes Gr. 4-6
SST1-12A	Snow Gr. JK/SK
SST1-12B	Snow Gr. 1
SST1-12C	Snow Gr. 2-3
SSB1-76	Solar System Gr. 4-6
SSPC-44	South America B/W Pictures
SSA1-11	South America Gr. 4-6
SSB1-05	Space Gr. 2-3
SSR1-34	Spelling Blacklines Gr. 1
SSR1-35	Spelling Blacklines Gr. 2
SSR1-14	Spelling Gr. 1
SSR1-15	Spelling Gr. 2
SSR1-16	Spelling Gr. 3
SSR1-17	Spelling Gr. 4
SSR1-18	Spelling Gr. 5
SSR1-19	Spelling Gr. 6
SSR1-27	Spelling Worksavers #1 Gr. 3-5
SSM1-02	Spring Celebration Gr. 2-3
SST1-01A	Spring Gr. JK/SK
SST1-01B	Spring Gr. 1
SST1-01C	Spring Gr. 2-3
SSM1-01	Spring in the Garden Gr. 1-2
SSB1-26	Squirrels Gr. 3-5

Code #	Title and Grade
SSB1-112	Stable Structures & Mechanisms 3
SSG1-05	Steps in the Research Process 5-8
SSG1-02	Stock Market Gr. 7-8
SSN1-139	Stone Fox NS Gr. 4-6
SSN1-214	Stone Orchard NS Gr. 7-8
SSN1-01	Story Book Land of Witches Gr. 2-3
SSR1-64	Story Starters Gr. 1-3
SSR1-65	Story Starters Gr. 4-6
SSR1-73	Story Starters Gr. 1-6
SSY1-09	Story Writing Gr. 1-3
SSB1-111	Structures, Mechanisms & Motion 2
SSN1-211	Stuart Little NS Gr. 4-6
SSK1-29	Subtraction Drills Gr. 1-3
SSY1-05	Subtraction Gr. 1-3
SSY1-11	Successful Language Pract. Gr. 1-3
SSY1-12	Successful Math Practice Gr. 1-3
SSW1-09	Summer Learning Gr. K-1
SSW1-10	Summer Learning Gr. 1-2
SSW1-11	Summer Learning Gr. 2-3
SSW1-12	Summer Learning Gr. 3-4
SSW1-13	Summer Learning Gr. 4-5
SSW1-14	Summer Learning Gr. 5-6
SSN1-159	Summer of the Swans NS Gr. 4-6
SSZ1-02	Summer Olympics Gr. 4-6
SSM1-07	Super Summer Gr. 1-2
SSN1-18	Superfudge NS Gr. 4-6
SSA1-08	Switzerland Gr. 4-6
SSN1-20	T.V. Kid NS. Gr. 4-6
SSA1-15	Take a Trip to Australia Gr. 2-3
SSB1-102	Taking Off With Flight Gr. 1-3
SSN1-55	Tales of the Fourth Grade NS 4-6
SSN1-188	Taste of Blackberries NS Gr. 4-6
SSK1-07	Teaching Math Through Sports 6-9
SST1-09A	Thanksgiving JK/SK
SST1-09C	Thanksgiving Gr. 2-3
SSN1-77	There's a Boy in the Girls... NS 4-6
SSN1-143	This Can't Be Happening NS 4-6
SSN1-05	Three Billy Goats Gruff NS Gr. 1-3
SSN1-72	Ticket to Curlew NS Gr. 4-6
SSN1-82	Timothy of the Cay NS Gr. 7-8
SSF1-32	Titanic Gr. 4-6
SSN1-222	To Kill a Mockingbird NS Gr. 7-8
SSN1-195	Toilet Paper Tigers NS Gr. 4-6
SSJ1-35	Toronto Gr. 4-8
SSH1-02	Toy Shelf Gr. P-K
SSPC-24	Toys B/W Pictures
SSN1-163	Traditional Poetry Gr. 7-10
SSH1-13	Transportation Gr. 4-6
SSW1-01	Transportation Snip Art
SSB1-03	Trees Gr. 2-3
SSA1-01	Tropical Rainforest Gr. 4-6
SSN1-56	Trumpet of the Swan NS Gr. 4-6
SSN1-81	Tuck Everlasting NS Gr. 4-6
SSN1-126	Turtles in Literature Gr. 1-3
SSN1-45	Underground to Canada NS 4-6
SSN1-27	Unicorns in Literature Gr. 3-5
SSJ1-44	Upper & Lower Canada Gr. 7-8
SSN1-192	Using Novels Canadian North Gr. 7-8
SSC1-14	Valentines Day Gr. 5-8
SSPC-45	Vegetables B/W Pictures
SSY1-01	Very Hungry Caterpillar NS 30/Pkg 1-3
SSF1-13	Victorian Era Gr. 7-8
SSC1-35	Victorian Christmas Gr. 5-8
SSF1-17	Viking Age Gr. 4-6
SSN1-206	War with Grandpa SN Gr. 4-6
SSB1-91	Water Gr. 2-4
SSN1-166	Watership Down NS Gr. 7-8
SSH1-16	Ways We Travel Gr. P-K
SSN1-101	Wayside Sch. Little Stranger NS 4-6
SSN1-76	Wayside Sch. is Falling Down NS 4-6
SSB1-60	Weather Gr. 4-6
SSN1-17	Wee Folk in Literature Gr. 3-5
SSPC-08	Weeds B/W Pictures
SSQ1-04	Welcome Back – Big Book Pkg 1-3
SSB1-73	Whale Preservation Gr. 5-8
SSH1-08	What is a Community? Gr. 2-4
SSH1-01	What is a Family? Gr. 2-3
SSH1-09	What is a School? Gr. 1-2
SSJ1-32	What is Canada? Gr. P-K
SSN1-79	What is RAD? Read & Discover 2-4
SSB1-62	What is the Weather Today? Gr. 2-4
SSN1-194	What's a Daring Detective NS 4-6
SSH1-10	What's My Number Gr. P-K
SSR1-02	What's the Scoop on Words Gr. 4-6
SSN1-73	Where the Red Fern Grows NS 7-8
SSN1-87	Where the Wild Things Are NS 1-3
SSN1-187	Whipping Boy NS Gr. 4-6
SSN1-226	Who is Frances Rain? NS Gr. 4-6
SSN1-74	Who's Got Gertie & How...? NS 4-6
SSN1-131	Why did the Underwear ... NS 4-6
SSC1-28	Why Wear a Poppy? Gr. 2-3
SSJ1-11	Wild Animals of Canada Gr. 2-3

Publication Listing

Code #	Title and Grade	Code #	Title and Grade	Code #	Title and Grade	Code #	Title and Grade
SSPC-07	Wild Flowers B/W Pictures						
SSB1-18	Winter Birds Gr. 2-3						
SSZ1-03	Winter Olympics Gr. 4-6						
SSM1-04	Winter Wonderland Gr. 1						
SSC1-01	Witches Gr. 3-4						
SSN1-213	Wolf Island NS Gr. 1-3						
SSE1-09	Wolfgang Amadeus Mozart 6-9						
SSB1-23	Wolves Gr. 3-5						
SSC1-20	Wonders of Easter Gr. 2						
SSB1-35	World of Horses Gr. 4-6						
SSB1-13	World of Pets Gr. 2-3						
SSF1-26	World War II Gr. 7-8						
SSN1-221	Wrinkle in Time NS Gr. 7-8						
SSPC-02	Zoo Animals B/W Pictures						
SSB1-08	Zoo Animals Gr. 1-2						
SSB1-09	Zoo Celebration Gr. 3-4						